My Weekly

2022 ANNUAL

PAGE
12

PAGE
40

PAGE
62

FICTION

CELEBRITY

FANCY THAT

SPICY BISCUIT BONANZA

BRAINBOOSTERS

DC THOMSON
MEDIA

Kindness And Love

…things we all hope to have in our lives – these high-profile personalities and charities show us the way

2022 is a very special year, with HM The Queen's Platinum Jubilee marking 70 years of devotion to our country. Her reign, the longest of any British sovereign, has been a constant through major world milestones and huge shifts in cultural norms.

As Princess Elizabeth, she proclaimed her intent on her 21st birthday in 1947. "I declare before you all that my whole life, whether it be long or short, shall be devoted to your service… But I shall not have the strength to carry out this resolution alone, unless you join in it with me."

Jubilee celebrations are planned for early June, allowing us to pay tribute to her extraordinary, lifelong service.

Picking Up The Baton

◆ **The Countess of Wessex** is patron to 70 different charities and organisations at home in the UK, and worldwide. She often quietly involves herself in humanitarian causes without any media fanfare, such as the frequent help she gave in packing and delivering food parcels during the Covid-19 pandemic.

◆ **Prince William**'s parents both ensured that he understood the importance of charitable work from an early age. As an adult, he and the Duchess of Cambridge are now setting a fine example to their own family with their involvement, together and individually, with multiple good causes, at home and abroad. ➡

Celebrities With A Heart

Those who have put their own good fortune to work for others, through charities and good causes

Dolly's Lolly

Affairs of the heart have inspired songs that have brought **Dolly Parton** global fame, creating a fortune that the generous singer has shared with good causes in Tennessee and beyond. Dolly also donated $1 million to help fund research into a vaccine for the Covid-19 virus.

Bravo Boys

◆ Among multiple charitable works, the **Elton John** AIDS Foundation has raised over $450 million since it was founded in 1992.

◆ **George Clooney** awarded fourteen close friends $1 million each, to thank them for their support in his early acting years.

◆ The world-leading **Michael J. Fox** Foundation for Parkinson's Research was established by the popular actor and has funded $1 billion of research programmes to date.

Go Joe!

Joe Wicks has been an inspiration to those trying to keep fit and also to fundraisers everywhere. In 2020, the curly-haired fitness guru raised £580,000 for our frontline health heroes during lockdown and over £1m for his 24-hour charity workout with the BBC's *Children in Need.* ➡

WORDS: CLAIRE SAUL PICTURES: SHUTTERSTOCK, ISTOCKPHOTO

Poppy Power

When the very first Poppy Appeal began in 1921, poppy sales raised funds to aid housing and employment for veterans. In recent (non-pandemic) years we've purchased over 40 million paper poppies through the annual Royal British Legion Poppy Appeal, raising millions of pounds to support members of the Armed Forces community.

Several million of today's poppies are handmade by a small team of disabled veterans and their dependants, home-workers and volunteers at The Poppy Factory in Richmond. The team also produces Remembrance symbols for the Field of Remembrance at Westminster Abbey and thousands of wreaths and sprays for members of the Royal Family, military organisations and memorial events, including the rectangular wreath placed around the grave of the Unknown Warrior at Westminster Abbey.

Since November 1920, this grave has represented the thousands of unidentified casualties of the First World War. In 1923, Lady Elizabeth Bowes Lyon, who we'd later recognise as the Queen Mother, placed the bouquet from her marriage ceremony to the future King George VI, on this spot. Since then, royal brides marrying at Westminster Abbey, and elsewhere, have done the same.

Charities Reaching Out

...to offer support, help and guidance to people in need, the vulnerable, the carers and the heroes

Helping Hands

Age UK supports older people through companionship, advice and support. The organisation operates at a national level and a network of local offices to provide advice on subjects including health, care and legal issues and among their services, offer telephone befriending and social activities.
Age UK also campaign against issues affecting quality of life in later age.
www.ageuk.org.uk

Welcoming Arms

Over 65,000 children live with almost 55,000 foster families across the UK each day. The Fostering Network, the UK's leading fostering charity, aims to bring together everyone involved in the lives of fostered children. The charity works to improve opportunities for fostered children, to provide expert guidance and share best practice on all aspects of fostering services and to champion the practice of fostering. **www.thefosteringnetwork.org.uk**

Helen Lederer

The Kindness Of Cats

**Disaster strikes after Carole has been persuaded
to do her rather nice new boss a feline favour…**

I'm perfectly fine on my own, Carole told herself, before placing her yucca plant in front of the offending cat flap to take her mind off Smokey.

Perhaps it was time to count her blessings. She was supposed to count them every morning according to the American life coach on her mindfulness app, so Carole duly began counting.

"I've got my dream job, a smashing new flat with a garden for heaven's sake, not to mention the most lush new sofa in the world – and the last thing I need is being responsible for a cat."

She said this out loud and to no one in particular, since she was now living alone in a one-bedroom flat. There was no scope for a lodger, even if she wanted one. She put the kettle on and began unwrapping her mother's house-warming gift. The package had been slipped into her holdall at the last minute along with a huge slab of smelly cheese to "keep you going for the journey".

Carole sighed and placed the merry cat-themed tea towels face down on the dishwasher. Was this on purpose? Was her mother hinting she should get another cat now she'd left home? Did she think her daughter would miss Smokey so much?

No way will I become a spinster cat lady, thought Carole, as she went into the sitting room to rearrange her favourite velvet cushions on the new sofa. She stood back to admire the effect. The sofa really was very inviting. Perhaps she'd meet someone special in the coming months and they could cosy up together. Maybe they'd hunker down with a tartan throw for the cold winter evenings?

She was still young enough to settle down. Even if she had wasted the last five years with a completely unsuitable man who'd had the cheek to take Smokey with him when he disappeared to Australia. When she was being rational, she could see the logic in it. Smokey was his cat. And anyway, she couldn't afford to fly all the way to Sydney to exert visiting rights.

No, things couldn't be better. She wasn't lonely at all. No regrets about Smokey. And at least she was working with one of her best friends at an exciting new marketing agency. They made a great team, and so what if Frances had just got herself engaged to an accountant? ➤

No, things couldn't be better. She wasn't lonely at all. No regrets about Smokey

There'd still be plenty of time to have girly fun. This was a new start. No unsuitable man and no cat.

After a soak in the bath and a change of clothes, Carole felt much calmer. She tonged her hair to attempt a slightly tousled look she'd seen in a magazine, before deciding on a black slip dress that showed off her figure. Who knew that being chucked would lead to such honed calf muscles and a flatter stomach?

And anyway, there was something quite inspiring about doing her five laps round the park, wearing headphones, and being told by the American coach to count her blessings every day. More people should do it.

replaced the boots with trainers. And she agreed with Frances; Granny's jacket was more Glyndebourne than a south London wine bar. It had been so long since she'd been out with friends, she'd forgotten how to do it.

She stuffed her tousled hair into a knitted beanie hat and pulled on a pair of jeans to tone it all down. The silk dress would just have to be stuffed inside the jeans since it was a bit tight to wriggle out of, and Frances was quite good at breaking things if left alone for too long.

"Slight spillage," explained Frances, as she mopped up some water with a smiley cat tea towel. She turned to face her friend.

"That's still quite a strange look if you

Might it be one of those meetings when a couple just clicked? Did that happen?

Carole grabbed her jacket to cover the slip dress on the way to answer the door. She knew she didn't want to be too "out there' with her new figure – on the other hand she didn't want to freeze.

"Hmmm. Off to the opera, are we?" said Frances, looking her friend up and down and laughing.

Carole quickly removed her grandmother's jacket. To be fair it was quite padded in the shoulder area, and the fox around the neck had invited controversy in the past. Her grandmother had told her it was fake, and she'd decided to believe that.

"Happy housewarming, Carole!" said Frances, striding towards the kitchen with a bunch of flowers.

"Thank you, they're lovely! I'll just go and remove… change…"

Maybe the high suede boots were a bit bold for a first outing with work mates. Carole immediately pulled them off and

don't mind me saying. Mind you, last time we all got together Derek turned up in a waterproof poncho."

Carole felt nervous. She'd forgotten she hadn't met her team leader yet. Derek had been away on a conference during her first week and in any case, it had been his deputy who had given her the actual job. What if Derek thought she might be a poor choice? But Frances was now staring at the kitchen door.

"What is it?" asked Carole, now having doubts about the whole evening.

"Why have you got a stonking great plant blocking out all the light?" Frances abandoned the flower arranging and shoved the yucca plant far away from the door. "Much better."

The evening in the wine bar went surprisingly well. The team were really friendly, Frances's fiancé wasn't quite as dull as Carole remembered and

Frances to see whether he was with anyone special.

"Right, I'd better be going, folks." Derek stood up and put a twenty-pound note on the table for the next round.

"You got the last round," said Frances, handing the money straight back to him.

"My mother's panicking," Derek explained apologetically.

Carole tried not to look relieved.

"I'm taking her to Madrid tomorrow evening, and she thinks I'd forgotten."

"Had you?" asked Frances.

"Sort of." He smiled and looked across at Carole.

"Holiday to Madrid?" Carole felt she was allowed one question, even though they had just met.

Derek shook his head.

"Family duty to Madrid. Her sister lives there. A few days always do the trick."

"Well, maybe we should all make a move then." Fran and her fiancé were clearly wanting to be alone. Carole would have suggested that they get a room, but she didn't know the fiancé well enough.

"Oh, wait. What about Dave?" said Derek suddenly.

Carole allowed herself to feel worried again. Was Dave Derek's love child?

"I need someone to look after him."

"Can't you get a cat sitter?" mumbled Frances' fiancé, as he helped Frances into her coat and kissed her neck at the same time. Carole tried not to feel jealous. And anyway, Derek had a cat called Dave which meant he might still be single.

"I couldn't do that to him," said Derek.

Frances looked at Carole.

"Carole's got a cat flap."

"But…"

"Don't deny it. I saw it this evening. I'll text you her address Derek. Perfect plan."

She and her fiancé moved towards the door, holding hands

"Yes but… I mean, yes I have…" ➤

even Derek turned out to be quite nice. Well – very nice, in fact. He was quiet, but whenever he said anything, everyone listened to him.

As the evening wore on, the two of them soon struck up an easy alliance against Frances and began teasing her. Carole even decided to come clean about the doubtful origins of her grandmother's fur jacket which made him laugh loudly.

His laugh was unexpectedly thrilling and when they both went up to the bar to buy drink at the same time, Carole couldn't help but notice his tall, strong physique. Might this be one of those meetings when a couple just clicked? Did this sort of thing still happen?

When they both returned to the table, Derek checked his phone. Carole's heart sank. She should have checked with

Derek looked at her. There was hope in his eyes.

"It would only be for a few days…"

Everyone looked at Carole.

"OK," she said.

"Great!'

"Actually, I'm a but rusty in the cat department –" Carole began to say to Derek, in case he had any expectations, but everyone was now outside on the pavement and he was already on his bike and riding off into the night.

Derek turned up at her flat the next morning with a basket containing a small tabby cat who was peering out with understandable suspicion.

Carole had re-arranged her cushions five times already and sprayed herself with a new perfume.

"Coffee?' she asked casually.

"No time, sorry…"

"Oh."

"When I come back, perhaps? This is really kind of you, Carole."

The way he said *Carole* made her feel quite lightheaded.

"Dave might be a little skittish at first."

"What does that mean?"

"Well… skittish'

"Right. So maybe we should let Dave get used to me gradually, and… to any new smells…"

Derek smiled at her. Carole turned away. Maybe she'd overdone the perfume.

"Just one coffee?" he said.

Carole busied herself with the cafetière and tried not to spill anything in her excitement. Derek sat down at the table and watched Dave explore the kitchen and make himself at home.

A few hours later, Carole found herself with one hand on the latch of her front door so she could say goodbye slowly, and hoped against hope that Derek might decide on a token kiss.

After all, he was leaning in and she could sense how close he was…

Suddenly there was a vibrating sound.

"My mother.'' Derek waved his phone at her sheepishly.

"Oh."

"Can we pick up where we left off when I get back?"

"We can."

"Till then?"

"Till then."

As Carole closed the door, she felt dizzy. Within weeks she'd moved to London, moved into a new flat (with a cat flap), met a wonderful man, and was now in charge of his cat…

It was almost too much. She decided to allow herself a little nap, only to wake up with a start some time later at the sound of next door's children playing outside after school.

"Dave? Davey, Davey, where are you?"

She checked the cat flap. Oh no – she'd left it open. She should have closed it for Dave's first few hours in a strange place. Now he'd bolted – and it was all her fault. What if he didn't return?

The next few days went by in a blur. Carole didn't dare tell anyone at work that her new charge had gone missing. Instead, she put notices up on trees and asked all her neighbours to look out for a very sweet, small, skittish tabby cat.

It had all been going so well, and now she'd ruined it. But she had to keep going. She decided to invest in the best cat food money could buy and leave it outside the cat flap every night and morning. And even though the food was always eaten, which was a positive, she couldn't be sure who was eating it. Maybe it was a fox?

Carole had to assume that Derek might never want to speak to her again. This made sense. But would that situation mean that she'd lose her job?…

Derek nodded. Carole had put out a plate of biscuits to soften the blow.

"Not here," he repeated and bit into a shortbread finger.

"No, I… I left the food here." Carole pointed to the kitchen door and showed him where she had positioned the dish. She was playing for time.

Derek suddenly called out, "Dave, Dave, where are you? Come on, you little tinker."

"Excuse me," said Carole and fled to the bathroom. Ten minutes later she unlocked the door, having decided to confess everything.

"Derek?" she began, but then stopped when she reached the sitting room.

Derek and Dave were now curled up

She showed him where she'd positioned the dish. She was playing for time

On and on went her spiralling thoughts.

Finally, it was the day of reckoning. She knew it was Derek who was ringing the doorbell. He had texted her from the airport. She opened the door. He was even smiling at her.

"I've been thinking about this moment all week…"

Then he pulled her towards him and hugged her. Carole decided to enjoy the feeling, while she could.

"So how was Dave?"

"Dave?" Carole swallowed hard and began walking towards the kitchen

"Yes. Was he skittish?"

Derek was close behind her. She could smell aftershave. Was that for her benefit?

"Yes – he was a bit, actually."

"And?"

"And… he's not here."

together on her sofa.

"He goes away sometimes, but he always comes back," said Derek, eyeing her carefully.

Carole nodded. Maybe Derek knew. She couldn't be sure but she decided to join them on the sofa anyway.

"Well, I'm not going away again for a good while… are you?" he asked softly.

Suddenly he pulled her towards him. They lay there together for some time.

"No, I'm not going anywhere," murmured Carole, into his chest.

At this, Dave decided he'd had enough and hopped off the sofa. Clearly he, for one, was going somewhere.

Carole couldn't be sure, but had Dave given her a little wink? Ⓜ

Turn overleaf for our Author Interview ➙

Red Letter Days

Helen recalls her literary successes, and shares the tension of the days when she struggles to write

My magic moment… was when I was ten years old. My teacher had asked the class to write a story about an imaginary fishing village. We had been studying Dylan Thomas and my imagination was rather fired up. Two days later, the teacher decided to read out two of the best stories. Mine was one! I'd been struggling until then. Hearing my story read out made me so grateful for her belief in me.

My first acceptance: I sent off the synopsis for *Losing It* to my publishers seven years ago. When it was accepted, I was over the moon. I knew I had to write this novel. I'd already abandoned a previous novel which had been painful. The publisher's confidence in me spurred me on. The pleasure in reading bits of my book to audiences at literary festivals felt as exciting as my first stand-up comedy gigs. I felt I'd come full circle. And the fact that the novel was nominated for the PG Wodehouse Comedy Literary Prize was as unexpected as it was thrilling.

Writing during lockdown: It has been intense. I am writing my memoir and it has been painful to revisit some times in my life. Combined with the isolation we are all experiencing, the temptation to ruminate about the past is always there. It helps to go for walks, but I make myself return to the desk or I start fretting! It's been hard to concentrate on reading other books, which is usually helpful. Sometimes a binge on a box set can make me write better next day. Guilt is a great motivator.

Where I write: I moved my computer into my daughter's old bedroom. It is the furthest away from the trampoline in next door's garden. I need silence for writing, so exuberant cries of children are not ideal. My daughter's teenage diaries are in the drawers, but I don't look at them. I might ask her to show me one day!

My inspiration: I love hearing of authors who became published at a later age. The kind of writer who writes because they simply have to. And who don't give up. Victoria Wood has been an inspiration. Her biography was so revealing about how long it took her to find her place in the world, and her love of the 'right' words.

My writing mantra: 'Screw it, just do it'. Never leave the desk without a deposit of at least 500 words. Every word will trigger another word. Editing can provide the sparkle, the first outlay is the passion.

I founded a literary prize called Comedy Women in Print. The unpublished winner wins a publishing deal, and the published winner receives lots of deserved attention. I'm determined to shine a light on witty women's writing. Year three is looking very exciting. We love the support from audiences online. We need to laugh at funny fiction more than ever. 🅜🅦

✦ In 1959, *Ben Hur* set all kinds of records! It is in a three-way tie for having won the most Oscars raking in a staggering 11 trophies.

✦ Russell Crowe stars as *Noah*, the man who built an ark to save humanity from the floods, in the movie of that name in 2014.

✦ **Esther and the King** in 1960 recounts the origin of the Jewish celebration of Purim, and stars a pre-Dynasty Joan Collins in the titular role.

✦ *The Nativity Story* from 2000 tells the story of Jesus' birth, and was the first feature film to premier at the Vatican.

✦ 1965's *The Greatest Story Ever Told* tells the story of Christ's life from beginning to end and was originally 4 hours and 20 minutes long!

✦ The inimitable Richard Burton starred in *The Robe* in 1953 as Marcellus who has to grapple with life-changing guilt after he wins the Messiah's robe in a game of dice.

FANCY THAT!

Fascinating facts on **Biblical Movies!**

✦ 1961's *Barabbas,* follows the criminal set free in place of Jesus and is probably most famous for filming the crucifixion scene during an actual solar eclipse.

✦ *The Passion of the Christ* in 2004 was Mel Gibson's controversial pet project covering the final 12 hours of Jesus' life, with flashbacks.

✦ *Jesus Christ Superstar* in 1973 was based on the Andrew Lloyd Webber/Tim Rice rock musical, telling the story of the weeks before Christ's death and his conflicts with Judas.

✦ *Prince of Egypt* was an animated movie showing a sympathetic Ramses and featuring the voices of Val Kilmer, Ralph Fiennes, Michelle Pfeiffer and Sandra Bullock

Cecil B DeMille's *The Ten Commandments* starring Charlton Heston in 1956 takes the number 6 spot in all-time box office numbers

Christmas Wishes

New traditions can work just as well as old ones – and it seems Emma's festive magic is a sweet success

By Gill Charnock

The smell of warm cinnamon drifted through the hatch of the family-run bakery.

"Oh, that smells of Christmas," Emma commented peeping through the hatch into the kitchen.

"Fresh cinnamon buns," Christine said as she brought the tray through to the shop and placed them next to the iced fingers and chocolate eclairs. It was only a small shop but it was tightly packed with pastries all laid out on dated countertops and shelves. French bread sticks stood regimentally to attention in baskets on the well-worn black and white tiled floor.

"Where are all our customers?" Christine asked, pushing a strand of hair off her face as she looked into the empty shop, her face looking sad as she spoke.

"We need more customers; we should be busier than this coming up to Christmas." Emma, always fearful of them having to give up their business, agreed with her sister. They had only been open a few months and

Emma was beginning to wonder if they had made a mistake. They both had a passion for baking and when the old butcher's shop came up for rent, they had jumped at the opportunity to open a bakery together. They had sunk their joint savings into it. So, they had to make a go of it.

Christine walked towards the shop door, the glass fogging as she peered out onto the busy high street full of busy Christmas shoppers, their bags laden with gifts. A slate-grey sky hung heavy with snowflakes that would soon have everyone rushing home.

"Emma?" Christine turned to her sister. "I know it's cold, and it may even snow, but what do you think about leaving the shop door open so the wonderful aroma of those cinnamon buns can drift out into the street and draw in a few more customers?"

"Good idea," replied Emma, "I could do a window display." Feeling inspired, she wrote a display card to accompany them.

Buy a Cinnamon bun and make a Christmas Wish with every bite.

The sound of distant carol singers

drifted in through the open door as she placed the buns in the centre of the window. Then wrapping her cardigan tightly around her slim body, she went outside to inspect her display. She was feeling pleased with herself when a small boy dressed in school uniform stopped to look in the window.

"Can you make any wish?" he asked, looking up at Emma.

"I don't see why not," she replied.

She went along with him; after all, they needed every customer they could get.

He bounced into the shop, rubbing his hands together as if he was about to receive a very large Christmas present.

"Don't forget to make a wish with every bite," she quickly added as he left the shop.

"One bun sold – only twenty-three more to go," Emma said.

"And only a few hours in which to do it," Christine added.

"Well if we run out, you'll just have to make more," Emma joked back.

It smells wonderful in here," said a rather well-dressed young man as he entered the shop, briefcase firmly clutched in his hand. "I'll take two cinnamon buns, please."

"Certainly," replied Christine, feeling triumphant as she dropped two buns into a paper bag. "Don't forget to make a wish with every bite." She was getting into the spirit of it now. ➜

Joel Edwards left the shop feeling pleased with himself. He needed this wish and even though he did not believe in such things, he was prepared to give anything a go if it fulfilled his long-held dream.

"I have a lovely dessert for us," he said, placing the two buns on the kitchen worktop of the flat he shared with his girlfriend Maggie.

They had been together for over seven years, and not a day went by when he did not ask her to marry him… but she always turned him down.

"Why change things when they are working so well?" she would say.

He had fallen in love with her even though she was not his usual type. She was a little on the wild side for him. As an accountant, he liked everything – just like the figures he worked with – to be orderly, balanced, and correct.

Maggie, on the other hand, was the

He immediately fell silent, wide-eyed.

"If it keeps him quiet, I'll be back tomorrow for a dozen more," she said as she winked at Emma.

"Don't forget to make a wish," she called out as the woman reached the doorway.

"Oh, I already had my wish," she said, looking down with a smile at the contented child in the pushchair.

Later that afternoon the two sisters stopped for a break.

"What would you wish for?" Emma asked Christine as she slid a cinnamon bun across to her.

"It's quite simple really – that our business does well."

"Well, I'd wish that too," said Emma. "Because I don't want us to fail before we've had the chance to get started."

"But we need to come up with some ideas to get more regular customers in the

They bit into their buns, looked at each other and laughed

complete opposite; she was a free spirit, untidy and disorganised. But he never gave up asking her to marry him. He wanted what most men wanted when they got to a certain age – a wife and family – and these two little cinnamon buns were his last chance, because he could not spend another seven years asking her to marry him. He recited his wish over and over in his mind… then he took a bite and made his wish.

Back at the shop, the cinnamon buns were selling well.

"I'll take two cinnamon buns," said a rather robust-looking middle-aged woman with short, brown, curly hair as she burst in through the door pushing a crying child in a pushchair. She broke off a small piece and placed it firmly into the child's mouth.

shop," Christine said looking quite forlorn.

"We could hold a tasting evening where people can come and sample our lovely cakes and pastries. It would allow us to introduce ourselves to the neighbourhood and drum up some regular customers."

"Sounds like a good idea to me," Christine said smiling sweetly at her sister. "Anything that gets customers through the door is fine by me."

They bit into their buns, looked at each other and both laughed out loud.

"Well? Did you make your wish?" Emma asked.

Christine nodded. "This is daft, though. You've made all this up. There is no such tradition of wishing on a cinnamon bun."

"You're right," Emma replied, just as a couple of customers entered the shop, "but now I've started the tradition and we'll just have to carry on with it."

And with that, she pushed the last piece of her bun into her mouth and went out into the shop.

The next day Christine was up early, as usual, to make her now popular cinnamon buns. As promised, the woman with the pushchair returned for more.

"He loved the buns," she said, smiling. "It kept him quiet for ages but I'd better not let my daughter know. She would be furious if she knew I was feeding him all this sugar. I wouldn't want him to end up looking like me!" she said as she patted her rounded tummy.

"You must come along to our taster evening," Christine said as she slipped an invitation inside the bag. "You're one of our best customers."

"I just might do that," she said as she pushed the pushchair out of the shop.

"If we keep this up, we may just stay afloat," Christine said as she turned to Emma. "But once Christmas is over it may be a different story." Her smile faded.

The evening of the taster session soon came around and they were pleasantly surprised at how many people attended. The shop looked very festive with its Christmas decorations and as Christine looked around her at the twinkling Christmas lights, and the tables full of samples of her baking, she felt very proud at what they had accomplished.

Across the shop, Christine could see that Emma enjoying playing hostess. She was ushering over a familiar figure, this time without the pushchair.

"Thank you so much for the invitation. I'm Connie," she said, picking up a slice of Christine's angel cake. "It looks as if you've had a good turnout. If you ever need a cake decorator –" Connie continued between

bites – "just give me a call. I'll leave you my number. I was a wedding and celebration cake decorator before I gave it up to look after my grandson. Now he's starting nursery, I'd like to get back to work."

"I've never thought of doing wedding cakes!" Christine replied. "Maybe that's just what we need to bring in more business."

"It's good little earner," replied Connie, who was now tucking into a chocolate eclair. Christine began to wonder if she would have any cakes left to sell if she employed Connie, judging by the way she was eating her way through the samples.

She was still mulling this over when Joel and Maggie entered the shop.

"Hello. Do you do wedding cakes?" Maggie asked Christine with a note of urgency in her voice.

"Well, strangely enough," replied Christine, "we were just discussing that." she looked over to Connie, who was now happily devouring a currant bun.

"The thing is, we're getting married after Christmas and I need one in a hurry, I don't care how much it costs," she said looking up at Joel, his face beaming with happiness.

The evening was proving to be a sweet success – not only because it had given rise to a new business venture, but it appeared everyone's wishes were coming true.

Christine offered Connie a position on the spot, and she immediately abandoned her plate and sat down with Joel and Maggie to start planning their wedding cake.

The future was beginning to look bright for everyone – and it was all down to a wish on a cinnamon bun. ⓜ

• •

ACT OF KINDNESS

I live in a first floor apartment and I am lucky to have a lovely postman who on various occasions has kindly carried my numerous and heavy shopping bags up the stairs for me.

Oh My Darling

To Harry, sweetly fragrant clementines were the symbol of an unspoken love that could never be…

By Laura Madeleine

I *do not*, Harold Carew grumbled to himself, *want to go to the church's Christmas lunch.*

He was well aware of the event, had seen it advertised in the local paper: "a warm welcome and a free festive lunch, for anyone who needs it". *For the lonely*, he thought. And he wasn't lonely, he was just fine.

Still, he couldn't help but go slightly out of his way to walk past the church hall. He couldn't help but glance in at the windows, steamed with hot chocolate and breath and laughter, twinkling with coloured fairy lights. He couldn't help but hear the jingle of well-worn Christmas songs, couldn't help pausing on the pavement to breathe the scent spiralling from the church hall's kitchen. It was rich and savoury, whispering of wine and warmth and roast chestnuts.

haloes. He was happy; he always loved the festive season. Because in that freezing month, when it seemed as if the rock-hard soil would never sprout again, the citrus fruits arrived, carried on trains all the way from Spain, France, North Africa, some still bearing the leaves of the trees that grew them. They sang of sun, they lit up the little shop like ornaments of gold, and filled the air with zest.

That Saturday, he remembered his mother serving someone, a lady in a sumptuous fur coat and matching hat. Even at eight years old he could tell that the lady was rich, not their usual sort of customer. So when his mother bent down and gave him a clementine and told him to go and say Merry Christmas, he had been confused, until he saw the little girl waiting in the shadow of the cabbages for her mother to finish shopping. She looked a year or two younger than him, and although she wore a fine jacket and

The fruits sang of sun, and lit up the little shop like ornaments of gold

And beyond it, another scent, like a tiny firework on a dull day: sugary as nectar, fresh as the crystalline blue of the Mediterranean.

Oranges. No, not oranges, sweeter and gentler… Christmas clementines.

Abruptly, he was eight years old again, helping in the grocery shop on a chilly Saturday in December. Outside, thick smog had turned the strings of lights into glowing

expensive boots, she was staring at the floor, her face drawn and pale.

He remembered crossing the shop and holding out the clementine, like a magical orb from a fairy story.

"Merry Christmas," he said shyly.

The girl had looked up at him in surprise, her soft brown eyes wide. Inch-by-inch, she had begun to smile, an expression so hesitant and hopeful ➡

that he felt something swell in his chest.

"Merry Christmas," she whispered back, and took the fruit.

"Angela!" her mother had barked, and a second later they were hurrying out of the shop. He caught one glimpse of the girl, looking at him through the soot-speckled window, cradling the clementine to her chest, before she was gone.

"Excuse me?"

He realised he was standing stock still, blocking the pavement.

"Sorry," he muttered to the older lady wearing a red cardigan trying to get past.

"Not to worry," she said softly. "Merry Christmas."

He hunched into his coat and bustled away without a word.

No, he told himself as he walked, *I don't want to go to the Christmas lunch. I won't know anyone, and even if I did, I wouldn't know what to say.*

Once, he had been able to talk for England. He used to chatter day in, day out to customers and delivery drivers, schoolchildren and pensioners, to mothers and fathers with children on their hips and bags on their arms. Even as a teenager, he

had always known just the right thing to say; when to smile and when to nod in sympathy, when to lend a willing ear and when to wave aside a payment.

Except for once…

He had been fourteen, old enough to run the grocery shop alone, while his mother took a well-earned rest. December was always busy; his feet had ached after a long day, and he was looking forward to the cocoa and mince pies that waited at home. So he was annoyed when the bell had tinkled and a group of girls – giddy with frosty air and sugar – had spilled through the door.

"We're collecting for the needy of Saint Theresa's," one of them declared, jiggling a cardboard box that held a strange assortment of tinned meats and woollen hats. "Do you have anything to donate?"

He had smiled, knowing his mother would want him to give generously, and had filled a paper bag full of walnuts and shining hazelnuts. He had talked and joked with the girls until the shop was filled with laughter. Then, since it was December, he had offered each of them a clementine, with a sincere, "Merry Christmas".

"Merry Christmas," a voice had murmured back, and he found himself looking into a familiar pair of soft brown eyes. He had smiled, delighted to have met her again, and she had smiled too, opening her mouth to say something…

"Angela!" one of the girls called, dragging on her arm. "We'll be late!"

Angela, he thought, as she disappeared into the freezing afternoon. *I remember.*

Later, he found out from a friend that she came from the posh part of town; that she had been sent away to an expensive boarding school in Switzerland, and holidayed with her parents in summer, and only really returned home at Christmas.

He had shrugged and told himself it was foolish to think of her, and yet, whenever

paint, at the junk mail piling up behind the door like dead leaves, at the brash *TO LET* board. Once he was Harry Carew, proud proprietor, friend to the whole town. Now, he was just Carew, Mr, as the pharmacist so often called out.

He turned away abruptly, eyes stinging with tears, only to collide with a figure on the pavement behind him.

"Oh!" someone exclaimed as a box crashed to the ground, sending brightly coloured orbs rolling in all directions.

"I'm so sorry," he gasped.

"No, I'm sorry," a voice answered, "I wasn't paying attention.'

A young woman was smiling back at him. She had a round face beneath a pink knitted hat, and huge plastic spectacles.

His feet carried him on towards the site of all his happiness and heartbreak

he smelled the bright sweetness of a clementine, he thought of her eyes and her gentle smile, and her voice murmuring *Merry Christmas…*

Harold looked up and found he had been walking in the wrong direction. Rather than turning left towards his small terraced house, he had turned right towards the High Street. His feet had betrayed him, falling into their old route, as if trying to walk back into the past.

Ahead, the High Street looked merry. Colourful Christmas decorations festooned the lampposts, and there were fairy lights in all the shop windows, even the opticians. He knew he should turn away, return to his silent house, close the curtains against the cold, but his feet carried him on, towards the site of all his happiness and heartbreak.

In the darkening afternoon, the gold letters of the old sign sparkled:

Carew & Son, Greengrocer.

He stared at the windows clouded by

She was heavily pregnant, a padded jacket hanging on either side of her bump.

"Damn," she swore, stooping awkwardly to pick up the fruits. He bent to help as best he could. Once the clementines were all safely in the box, he took a step away.

"Thank you," the young woman said, "and Merry Christmas!"

He watched her go. The box was heavy, and she was obviously struggling.

It's none of your business, he told himself. But the sweet, cherished scent of clementines was on his hands, and the next thing he knew he was calling out, "Wait!"

"Here," he said, holding up his own string bag, "I'll help you carry some."

She sighed with relief.

"Thank you, that would be wonderful. I'm not going far, but I had no idea tangerines could be so heavy!"

"They're clementines, actually," he ventured shyly. ➡

"Oh?" The young woman squinted down into the box. "How can you tell?"

With the string bag full of fruit, they set off down the road together.

"Tangerines have a pebbly skin," he said. "And they're tart, slightly bitter. Clementines are smooth and sweet and shine like polished brass."

She laughed. "You know your oranges."

"I used to own the grocery shop, back there." He smiled. When was the last time he had talked to someone like this? He couldn't remember.

The young woman stopped dead. "You're Mr Carew? Harry Carew?"

"Yes," he answered warily, "how do you –?"

"But everyone talks about your old shop!" she exclaimed. "They say you used to have the best festive window in town."

He nodded, pleased. It was true; he had always been known for his Christmas decorations. It had started years ago, when, as a young man, he had badgered

called out from the back, "Just a minute!"

When he stepped into the shop, there she was. Although ten years had passed, he recognised her instantly. Angela. Her clothes were just as fine as ever, and yet she looked tired, with shadows beneath her eyes and lines of strain on her face. For a moment, he had been frozen in place, his heart trying to leap out of his chest. Then, she met his gaze. There was something unfathomable in her expression; sadness tumbled together with hope and longing.

"I saw the window display…" she said, before shaking her head, touching her cheek with one gloved hand. "I'm sorry, I'm being silly. I don't even need anything."

Her voice was low, refined like the announcers on the radio, but he could hear the heaviness of tears in it, like storm clouds. *Sit down,* he wanted to cry, *please, stay, and tell me what's wrong.* But she was already leaving, her head lowered, one hand on the door handle.

"Wait!"

She smiled, just a little. For one heart-stopping moment they were hand in hand

the local florist until she taught him how to make wreaths from pine and fir and holly, how to keep Christmas roses and poinsettias alive, how to arrange flowers.

Every year he had created a spectacular display of winter apples, cascades of hazelnuts, branches of sprouts, bouquets of carrots and parsnips, garlands of holly and mistletoe and above all, a huge pyramid of shining clementines. Each one a wish, an invitation, a reminder, in case she should ever pass by…

And one Christmas, in his twenty-fourth year, she had. Late in the day, when even the most hardened Christmas shoppers had sagged home, laden down with parcels, the bell above the door had rung, and he had

In three steps he was beside her. Before he could think twice, he took a clementine from the top of the pyramid in the window and placed it gently in her palm. She had looked back at him with tear-reddened eyes and smiled, just a little. For one, heart-stopping moment, they were hand in hand.

"Merry Christmas," he had whispered.

"Mr Carew?"

He blinked hard, and found himself back on the street, in the chill, grey present. The young woman had paused, and was frowning up at him.

"Mr Carew," she said again, "are you all right? You look miles away."

Years away, he thought, but nodded. They started to walk again.

"Do you," he cleared his throat, making an effort at conversation. "Do you live around here? I don't think I've seen you."

"I'm new." The young woman switched the box to the other arm. "My gran moved back a while ago. I'm staying with her."

"And your – ?" He stopped, not wanting to be rude.

"My partner?' the woman filled in easily. "We broke up, just after I found out I was pregnant. It was awful, but Gran's been a lifesaver. Anyway, she said she could use the company, otherwise she's all alone in that big old house."

He knew the feeling.

"Do you have anyone?" she asked.

"No. I was an only child and my father died young, so it was always just my mother and I."

"And you never married?"

"There was always the shop to think of," he murmured. The old excuse.

The woman looked sympathetic, but a moment later, her face brightened.

"Here we are."

He stared in astonishment. They were back at the church hall. The windows were still twinkling, the laughter and music still spilling from the door.

"Here…?"

"Yes, I promised to deliver these." The young woman led the way up the path. "It's tradition. Every year, Gran gives them out to everyone she knows." She looked back at him, and smiled. "Gran says they remind her of someone who was kind, when kindness was what she needed most."

With the words echoing in his head, he stepped through the door. At once, he was engulfed by music and warmth, the smell of hot sugar and cloves and port wine. A gentle nudge at his back propelled him in.

Around the room people were chatting, cups of coffee at their elbows and the debris of a convivial meal scattered over the cloths. Many were wearing paper hats and tinsel crowns, and at the front, someone was clearing chairs, making space for dancing.

"Gran!" The young woman called. "Look who I found!'

A person in a red cardigan – the same person who earlier had wished him Merry Christmas outside the hall – was rising from a chair and walking towards him. And all at once his eyes were misting over, because he knew that walk, that tilt of the head, that smile. He looked, disbelievingly, into a pair of soft brown eyes.

"Hello," Angela said, her expression just as bright as his, brimming with hope and happiness.

Hello, he wanted to cry, and *at last,* but he couldn't, he could only hold out a hand. Smiling, she took it, and suddenly they were surrounded by the scent of clementines, bringing memories of sweetness, and of a single act of love, never forgotten.

"Merry Christmas Harry," she said. 🆆

ACT OF KINDNESS

During the summer one of my neighbours decided to cheer everyone up… by making fresh pizza dough for the whole street! Each house had a mini pizza party and shared photos of their delicious creations.

Home For Christmas

In his parents' house for the holidays, Pete shrugged off his work persona and became the person he truly was

By Linda Lewis

E ven before Pete could put down his case, his mother enveloped him in a massive hug. "Happy Christmas!"

"Happy Christmas to you too," he replied. "Where's Dad?"

"In the front room, having a doze. Let me look at you." She stepped back. "Have you lost weight?"

Pete smiled. She said the same thing every time. "I don't think so, Mum. If I have, I'll put it back on before I leave. Where have you put me?"

She laughed. "Your old room. Same as always. Do you really need to ask?"

He didn't but he liked making her laugh. "Is there anything I can do?"

to be was a son. With a happy sigh, he plonked himself down on the bed and tugged off his expensive hand-made shoes. He spent a few moments wriggling his toes then reached under the bed where his favourite green monster slippers with their ridiculous talons were waiting in their usual place.

He'd just opened his suitcase when his mother knocked at the door.

"Come in, Mum. You don't have to knock," he said.

She put the hot chocolate on the bedside table then nodded towards the bed. The quilt cover showed a map of the British Isles. "Do you want me to change that? It's getting rather old."

"No thanks, Mum. It's perfect."

Pete could relax – he didn't have to be an executive, taking calls and doing deals

"No. It's all underway. Now go upstairs and get yourself settled. I'll bring you up a nice mug of hot chocolate."

"Thanks, Mum."

The second he stepped into his old room, a weight lifted from his shoulders. In his parents' house, he could relax. He didn't have to be an executive, taking calls and doing deals. All he had

"Good. Come down when you're ready. Dinner's at six."

He didn't have to ask what was cooking. The marvellous aroma of his mother's trademark slow cooked lamb had greeted him the moment he stepped through the door.

When he came out of the shower, his old dressing gown was hanging on the hook. It was blue and looked like ➡

Doctor Who's TARDIS, with the words *Police, Public call Box* written down the front in white capital letters.

His Mother had given it to him after his divorce.

"You can keep it here to remind you that even though you're in your forties, you're still my little boy."

After his had marriage unravelled, he'd felt so lost that he spent a week with his parents until the world started to make sense again.

He caught a glimpse of himself in the mirror. Wearing a silly blue dressing gown and monster slippers, he looked like a different man – felt like one too.

As he headed downstairs, he could smell the Christmas tree. In the living room, every surface was covered in tinsel, cards and twinkling lights. At home, he didn't bother with decorations. He treated his flat like a hotel room; all he did there was work and sleep.

He found his mother in the kitchen, making mint sauce.

"I'm so glad you could get away early," she said.

Last year, he'd arrived after dinner on Christmas Eve and left straight after breakfast on Boxing Day. His Mum hadn't said anything. She hadn't needed to because his father said it all for her!

As his dad had helped Pete carry his presents to the car, he'd lowered his voice. "You might not like Christmas son, but your mother does. If you can't spare us more than a day, then don't bother coming at all next year."

His father's words had struck home. It had taken a lot of juggling but he'd arranged to take a week off for the first time in years. This year, he didn't have to leave until late on the 29th.

As he slumped onto the sofa having eaten more than his fill, Pete was a very happy man. If only life could be like this all the time. Comfortable clothes, no worries, no emails, no conference calls.

He picked up his smart phone to check for messages just as his father came into the room.

"Can't you switch that thing off? Better still, let me put it somewhere safe. Then you won't be tempted to keep checking it." His father held out his hand

Pete switched off the phone and handed it over. "You know me too well. Thanks, Dad. It's great to be home."

That evening, they watched TV and played Scrabble. Time flowed past as easily as water in a stream.

In the morning, Pete woke in a panic until he remembered it was Christmas Eve. With a contented sigh he went back to sleep until the smell of a fried breakfast woke him at half past eight.

There was a cup of tea on the bedside table, still hot enough to drink. He swigged it down, threw on his dressing gown and slippers, then hurried downstairs, tugged by the smell of bacon.

"You shouldn't have gone to so much trouble," he said as his mother presented him with a plate piled high with bacon, eggs, mushrooms, baked beans, and hash browns.

"You don't eat properly when you're at your flat," she said. "Tell me, what did you have for breakfast yesterday? More than just a slice of toast?'

He nodded even though it wasn't true. He'd had to skip breakfast thanks to an early meeting.

After eating his fill, he patted his stomach and let out a contented sigh. "That was delicious, Mum. You must let me wash up."

When he tried to follow her into the kitchen, she stopped him with a look. "That's your father's job. I don't want him getting lazy!"

Pete chuckled. There wasn't much chance of that. His father had "retired" years ago. Now he did the accounts for a local charity, spent two days a week working in a charity shop, and helped out at a food bank at least once a month. On top of that, he maintained a fruit and vegetable garden and helped a friend with his allotment.

After they'd had their starters, he'd taken a call from a client. Kay wasn't amused. When it happened a second time, she put down her cutlery and waited until he'd finished talking, by which time her food was cold.

He'd apologised but it wasn't enough.

"When you're with me, I want you to be with me," she said, "not with your head still stuck in the office."

He'd promised to try harder but when it happened again on their next date, she said she didn't want to go out with him anymore.

The doorbell rang, jolting Pete's mind back to reality.

"I wonder who that could be," said his father. "Probably carol singers. We get a lot of those.'

"Aren't you going to answer it, then?" asked Pete.

His father shook his head. "Your mother likes to wait to see if they're actually going to sing something.'

"I'm sorry about you splitting with Kay. I know how much you liked her," Dad said

Washing up duties done, his father joined him on the sofa. "So, how's your love life, son?"

"Not great," Pete admitted.

"What happened with that woman you were dating? Kay wasn't it? She was your boss's PA?"

Pete nodded. His Dad was pushing eighty but there was nothing wrong with his memory. "We went out a couple of times, but she ended it."

"I'm sorry about that. I know how much you liked her."

"Still do," thought Pete.

As his Dad picked up the crossword, Pete's thoughts went back to his first date with Kay…

Only when the bell rang a third time, did he get up to go and answer it.

"You have a visitor," he said. "I'll go and help your mother, so you can talk.

When he saw who it was, Pete jumped to his feet.

"Kay! What are you doing here?"

"You're not answering your phone. I sent texts, emails… but nothing." She looked at his slippers, then shook her head as if to clear her mind of the image. "My boss needs to talk to you, actually. He says it's urgent. "

"What about?"

"Didn't you read the email?"

"No." He chuckled at the silliness of what he was about to say. "My dad ➤

confiscated my phone."

"Can't you get it back?"

Pete felt torn. Knowing Kay's boss, it would probably be something and nothing. Whatever it was, Pete wouldn't be able to do anything about it. All his suppliers were closed for the holidays.

He shook his head. "Tell him I'll deal with it when I get back to work."

"Do you really want me to say that?"

He nodded. "It's Christmas."

"He's not going to like it." She made the call. "Mr Wentworth, it's Kay. I'm with Pete. He's at his parents' place. He's on holiday until the 30th. I see… Yes, I understand…" She handed Pete the phone. "He wants to speak to you."

"Hi, Mr Wentworth. Happy Christmas.

hug. "It's great to have met you. Pete told us so much about you."

Kay gave a puzzled look. "He has?"

"Oh yes," she replied. Pete steered Kay into the hall before his mother could say anything else.

"Happy Christmas," he said but as he made to open the door, Kay stopped him.

"What you said in there, about being with somebody one hundred per cent, did you mean that?" Kay asked.

"I did."

She looked him up and down and shook her head as though she couldn't quite believe what she was seeing. "You're so different from how you are at work.

"You're so different here from how you are at work – which is the real you?"

I'm sorry about this but someone who means a lot to me said when I'm with people I should be with them, one hundred per cent. Right now, I'm with my folks… It's Christmas Eve. Kay should have finished work…" he checked his watch, "ten minutes ago… I see… That's great… You too. Bye." He handed the phone back to Kay. "Great. Here's Mum with the mince pies. You do like mince pies, don't you?"

"I love them," said Kay, "but I should be on my way. I'm going to my sister's. It's a long drive." She turned to Pete. "You're sure my boss was OK about this?"

"Yes." Pete grinned. "He said he forgot it was Christmas. Can you believe that?"

Kay smiled as Pete's mother came back with a bag full of mince pies. "To take with you," she explained. As she handed them over, she gave Kay a quick

Look at you – wearing monster slippers and a TARDIS dressing gown! I'm wondering which is the real you."

Pete rubbed his unshaven chin thoughtfully. "That's something else you taught me, to be myself when it really matters. I do it naturally when I'm here. I need to work on it the rest of the time.'

Kay smiled. "Next time we go out on a date, remind me to confiscate your phone."

As she drove away, Pete couldn't stop grinning. There was going to be another date. Ⓜ

•••••••••••••••••••••••••••••••••••

ACT OF KINDNESS

After major heart surgery my ex-husband was very weak, so I invited him to stay with me while he recovered. He had no appetite which made for a very weird Christmas.

Brain Boosters

Codeword

Each letter of the alphabet has been replaced by a number.
The numbers for the first name of our chosen celebrity are given.
Complete the puzzle to find out which production team produced
Jason Donovan's hit album *Ten Good Reasons*?

A B C D E F G H I J K L M N O P Q R S T U V W X Y Z

1	2	3	4	5	6	7	8	9	10	11	12	13
												A
14	15	16	17	18	19	20	21	22	23	24	25	26
		J						O		N		S

Turn To Page 159 For Solutions

| 26 | 4 | 22 | 19 | 25 | | 13 | 1 | 4 | 25 | 11 | 24 |
|S|O| | | | |A| | | | |N|

| 2 | 13 | 4 | 11 | 7 | 14 | 13 | 24 |
| |A| | | | |A|N|

With Love…

Amid the annoyances and rituals of daily life, there's something that makes Maisie stop and wonder

By Julie Goodall

I'm old. I don't need someone to tell me. I'm more than capable of knowing that all by myself. I've had eighty-three birthdays, two husbands, four children and goodness-knows how many grandkids.

I haven't lost my marbles just because I don't know how many grandkids there are. It's just hard to keep track, to be honest. Some of them live in another country, a ridiculously long way away. I haven't seen them for such a long time.

"I just want a bath. It's not much to ask. I know you're all busy but I'm quite capable of taking a bath on my own."

"Well, of course you are, Maisie, but let's get you a nice cup of tea. Perhaps you can take a bath later. Nearer bedtime? A bath nearer bedtime will help you sleep."

Now don't get me wrong. She's nice, is Colleen. A cute little thing from Ireland with a lovely, soft Celtic accent. She has

"Maisie? Where's your sock?"

I look down at my feet, cosy and warm in my Hello Kitty slippers, and she's right. One ankle is huddled inside a red sock patterned with Halloween cats and broomsticks, the other totally naked. I thought I'd been feeling a chill.

"Oh, that," I say, dismissing the absent item of clothing with a majestic wave of the hand. I imagine Queen Elizabeth II doing it, if her grandkids aren't behaving themselves. Although, that doesn't seem right. Weren't they grown-up now? For that matter, is The Queen still alive? Perhaps Charles is king?

"Any idea where it is, Maisie?"

I know better than to ask 'where what is?' I used to do that, before I cottoned on to what they were thinking. You ask a question like that and, before you know it, they've started calling you Dotty. I had an aunt once called Dotty. I'm pretty sure she worked for The Queen.

"I only put one sock on this morning. The other is still in the drawer"

only to open her mouth and I'm almost asleep. No need for a bath. But, a cup of tea? PG Tips is the answer to everything in this country. I imagine that if Jesus turns up, irritated off at the state of things, the staff at Rosewood Villas will sit him down with a Simpsons mug.

"It'll all look different, love, after a nice cuppa. Would you like a digestive to go with that?"

"Your sock? Where's your left sock?"

I knew if I stayed quiet long enough, I'd find out what we were looking for. I look down at my feet.

"I only put one on this morning," I explain, as though talking to an imbecile. "It's obvious, isn't it? The other is still in the drawer."

"Oh, so you only put one sock on, so you did? Why's that, Maisie?" ➡

I can tell Colleen doesn't believe me. Her glittery blue eyes are scanning the room and she stoops a little to glance under the bed.

My pulse races as my own gaze rests on the lamp. It's a fire risk. That's what they'll say it is. A red sock with Halloween cats and broomsticks has draped itself over the bulb.

"I think I would quite like a cuppa," I say slowly, wondering how it got on top of a standard lamp. I'm only four foot eleven on a good day due to my osteoporosis. "And a couple of digestives wouldn't go amiss either."

From Your Valentine xxx

Those extravagant capital letters are making me feel all warm inside

As she leaves the room, I watch the birds through the window, hopping in the sunshine and feeding from the table of seeds. The window is open a smidge and I wonder why I'm wearing one sock with Halloween cats and broomsticks on.

It doesn't feel like October. In fact, Christmas doesn't seem so far in the past.

On the windowsill, sits a large card. Intrigued, I cross the room with my Zimmer-frame, reach for the card and collapse into the armchair. It's a relief to take the weight off.

I used to go rambling and it feels like I walked the coastal path yesterday. Perhaps I did, although I'm not so sure I still possess walking boots.

The card has a big, puffy, satin heart on the front. My fingers tremble as I wonder why on earth I have a card like this in my room.

Inside are the words: *To my beautiful*

Maisie, Always my Valentine. From your Valentino Ted xxx

I stare at the words. The writing looks so familiar. Those extravagant capital letters making me feel all warm and funny inside. I place the card on the bed and determine to ask Colleen about it when she comes back.

In the meantime, I know I need to work out how to get that sock off the standard lamp.

"Ted," I whisper softly as I struggle back onto my feet. **MW**

....

ACT OF KINDNESS

In 2008, I underwent two big operations, in London. My auntie looked after me in her home after both, as my husband was working abroad – nine weeks in total! I will never forget her kindness.

120
Calories per
biscuit

RECIPE AND FOOD STYLING: JENNIE SHAPTER PHOTOGRAPHY: JON WHITTAKER

Jam Sandwich Biscuit Hearts

Ingredients (Makes 16)

- ◆ **200g plain flour**
- ◆ **100g butter, cut into pieces**
- ◆ **50g caster sugar**
- ◆ **½tsp mixed spice**
- ◆ **2 egg yolks, lightly beaten**
- ◆ **Few drops vanilla essence**
- ◆ **3tbsp each apricot and strawberry jam**
- ◆ **Icing sugar, for dusting, optional**

1 Sift the flour into a bowl and rub in the butter, until the mixture resembles fine breadcrumbs. Stir in the sugar and mixed spice. Add the egg yolks and vanilla essence and mix to a firm dough. Wrap in cling film and chill for 20min.

2 Preheat the oven to 200°C, Fan 180°C, Gas 6. Lightly grease 2 baking trays. Roll out the dough on a lightly floured surface until 4-5mm thick. Using a 5-5.5cm heart cutter, cut out an equal number of hearts. Cut out the centres of half the biscuits using a smaller heart or round cutter.

3 Roll out the centres to make more biscuits. Transfer the biscuits to the prepared trays and bake for 8-10min, until golden. Transfer to a wire rack to cool. Once completely cooled, sandwich biscuits together with jam – one intact and one cut-out. Dust with a little icing sugar, if wished, and serve.   **➜ 67**

My Funny Valentine

Sealed with a kiss, signed with a question mark… has Jacqui's face-saving ruse turned into a real mystery?

By Lynda Franklin

Most people, at some point in their lives, come across the age-old dilemma of whether or not it's acceptable to stretch the truth. At the age of fourteen, Jacqui decided that it most definitely was.

When you discover you are the only one among your friends who has not received a Valentine card, then it makes perfect sense to pretend you have. It's only a little white lie, after all. It doesn't hurt anyone, does it?

It was tricky to begin with, but over time Jacqui became quite expert in coming up with names of fictitious boys and laughing off questions about who may

And so her university years were much improved when it came to February 14. Jenny without fail would send her a card, sometimes beautiful, sometimes funny, sometimes plain, depending what she managed to grab in her lunch hour.

Jacqui didn't have to think of names because the cards were always signed with a great big question mark, and how was she to know who had sent it? How was she to know who liked her, but felt too shy to say so?

Jacqui, who previously found the whole run-up to Valentine's Day extremely stressful, could now relax in the certainty that at least one card would plop through her letter box on the day. Occasionally there were others, mostly

Jenny's cards still came. They came from Spain, Italy, Canada, cruise ships and hotels

have sent the non-existent card. It was the perfect solution to a potentially embarrassing problem, and right up to the day she left school Jacqui kept up the pretence. Then, far wiser and with a degree of maturity, she decided things had to change. Why pretend she had received a Valentine card? Why not simply make sure that she did? And who better to send it than her very best friend, Jenny?

jokey ones from fellow students, but it didn't matter. There would always be at least one sentimental, heart-filled card sitting on her shelf.

Jacqui was now almost thirty, single, and living in a pleasant, airy, top floor flat. Jenny's cards still came. They came from Spain, Italy and Canada. They came from cruise ships and boutique hotels. Jenny was a travel courier, and as busy as she

was, she never forgot the promise she had made to her good friend all those years ago. True, it was less of a lifesaving moment now and more of a joke between them, but they kept coming nevertheless.

Nice card, Jac." Edward lived downstairs in a one-bedroom flat. He described himself as a musician, but it was apparent why he had not made it to the dizzy heights of fame.

It was not for the want of practice. Jacqui was forced to listen to the loud crashing music below her night after night. If he wasn't so nice, she would probably have banged on the floor a few times by now. Probably he should give up all hope of becoming part of a successful rock band and get a sensible job, but Edward loved his guitar and was always waiting for the big break.

"Oh – thanks. Yeah, not sure who sent it." Jacqui slipped into her white lie routine effortlessly. "How about you? Did any of your many fans and admirers send you a card?"

Edward smiled. "No. Nothing for me."

"Oh well, better luck next year."

Edward shrugged. "Maybe."

"All a bit silly really, isn't it?" Jacqui warmed to her story. "I don't really take a lot of notice now." ➜

"You get a lot of them, then, do you?"

"I wouldn't say a lot – one or two a year, I suppose. Just a bit of fun, isn't it?"

"I wouldn't know. I've never had one."

This time Jacqui was genuinely surprised. "Really? What – never?"

Edward laughed. "I'm not bothered. I've got more important things to think about, like my gig tonight. I'm playing at The Swan. Are you coming? We're all meeting about eight."

She nodded. "Yes, I'll be there."

One of the band members who usually played at the pub was sick, and Edward had been offered a week's work. Tonight was a special Valentine's night and Jacqui and a group of friends were going along to support him.

As she got ready to go out, she found herself wondering how many Valentine's cards her friends had all received. Thank goodness Edward had seen hers. It was

began playing. It was loud, mostly in tune, and soon the whole pub was singing and swaying along.

Edward looked relaxed and happy.

His hair's far too long. He looks more like a hippy, she thought, drifting into imaging how it might look cut into a nice style. It was good hair, thick and wavy; it would probably look quite nice. She couldn't help smiling at his lanky frame moving around with his faithful guitar on his hip. He always looked his happiest when he was playing.

"He'll never make a rock singer, will he?" Lucy her friend was giggling.

"What do you mean? He's doing OK," Jacqui said, feeling a need to defend him.

"Face it, he's not a rock singer, Jac – never will be."

Her answer got lost in a loud cheer.

"Well, they seem to like him here," she said, trying to make herself heard. But she

His playing had driven her crazy. Yet she couldn't bring herself to moan at him

unusually impressive this year; Jenny had surpassed herself. She would have to congratulate her when she finally returned to England on finding such a nice one.

The pub was extra crowded and noisy tonight. Jacqui clutched a glass of wine and found a corner to stand in with her friends. Edward smiled at her from the small stage as he tuned up his guitar, and Jacqui waved back encouragingly.

She knew how nervous he felt whenever he performed, and really hoped he would be OK. He'd been practising hard for days and it had driven her crazy at times. Somehow, though, she just couldn't bring herself to moan at him.

Someone spoke into a microphone, followed by loud cheers, and the band

knew the crowd that met here every Saturday were happy to like anyone.

"He should just sing!" Lucy yelled.

"What?" Jacqui cupped an ear.

"He should stick to singing – you know – nice stuff. This rock music isn't him."

"Isn't it?"

"No – haven't you heard him sing? Properly, I mean. I think he was classically trained."

"Trained! Edward?"

Lucy laughed at Jacqui's expression and looked away. Jacqui turned back to the stage, gazing at Edward jumping around like a young gazelle on hot bricks. She couldn't help smiling. He loved this kind of music so much, but he was definitely off-key. She tried to imagine him singing sombre classical stuff.

In the break Jacqui managed to find a seat. Lucy plonked herself down next to her.

"So, go on, how many did you get?" she asked, smiling.

Jacqui laughed. "Just the one." It slipped off her tongue effortlessly. "What about you?"

"Three, but one of those was from my little brother, so two really."

"You beat me, then."

Jacqui didn't care. She had the beautiful floral card standing proud on her shelf. It was quality that mattered, and Jenny certainly bought quality.

"Who is it from?" Lucy asked.

"I've no idea! I must have an admirer!"

Lucy nodded, sipping her drink.

"You must."

The next morning the sound of Edward's guitar filtered up through the floor boards as usual. Jacqui took a swallow of coffee and sighed. Sunday morning. Really? Couldn't he at least wait until after lunch?

She finished her breakfast and got dressed. She'd have to have a friendly word with him, tactfully ask him to give them all a break from his twanging! Was that tactful? She laughed softly to herself. Probably not.

She tuned into the sound drifting up into her flat. He seemed to be playing something different today. It certainly wasn't sending the cat into a frenzy as it usually did! She promised herself one more coffee to ward off a threatening headache from last night, and then a relaxing day reading magazines and watching girlie films.

A knock on the door surprised her. No one called on Sunday mornings. Certainly Edward never knocked. He either walked straight in calling out his name, or yelled through the letter box.

It must be a proper visitor, which was annoying because the flat was a mess. She opened the door.

"Edward! Why are you knocking? You usually barge straight in."

He was wearing his usual jeans and T-shirt, seemed to have forgotten to brush his hair, and had his guitar over his shoulder. Without replying he began to strum a couple of chords, softly and tunefully.

"Shh, Edward, you'll wake everyone up. Come in for goodness' sake!"

He sauntered in, still playing. It was a melodious sound, nothing like the rock music he usually attempted to sing. She rolled her eyes, waiting for him to launch into one of his crazy songs, but he sat on the end of the sofa and carried on playing.

Then he began to sing, in a low throaty voice that didn't sound like him.

"*My funny Valentine, sweet comic Valentine…*"

OK, it was wasn't Frank Sinatra, but it was so sweet and unexpected, and she watched mesmerised as his fingers deftly stroked the strings in a slow rhythm. When he finished he looked up and ➔

shrugged.

"I guess that gives you a clue."

"Clue? What are you talking about? Edward that was beautiful. You have a beautiful voice when you sing like that."

"I like rock."

"Edward, you can really sing –"

"Never mind that, Jac. I sent the card."

"What?"

"Your Valentine card. I sent it."

"No, you didn't!"

He nodded, smiling. "I did. I should have told you before." He began to strum, holding her gaze, singing along softly to *My Funny Valentine* again.

"Wait!" Jacqui said suddenly. "There's something I have to do." She ran into

"You OK?" Edward put his guitar down. "Look. I understand if you're not interested but I thought this would be a good way to find out because – well, I like you, and would sort of like to know you even better." He gave a boyish grin and flicked hair from his face.

"So you sent me a Valentine card?" He nodded. "Yep." He didn't blush.

"I certainly didn't guess it was from you."

"Well that's the idea, I suppose."

"I suppose it is."

"But then I thought – well, if you don't ever know who it's from, there's not much point in sending it, is there?"

"I suppose not."

"So – " He gave a small shrug and placed his guitar gently on the floor. "Do you fancy dinner tonight with a rock star?"

"Well, I like you, and would sort of like to know you even better"

the bathroom, closed the door, and quickly rang Jenny.

A sleepy voice answered.

"This had better be life or death. Do you not know the time difference here?"

"Sorry, Jenny. Just tell me, did you send me a Valentine's card this year?"

"What? Yes, yes, of course I did. I always send one, you know that."

"One with hearts and flowers and a bird in the corner?"

"You did say you liked all that stuff."

"That card's definitely from you?"

"Unless you have two the same!"

"OK – right – thanks, Jenny. You can go back to bed now."

"Well, thank you." Her friend clicked off immediately.

Jacqui walked slowly back into the lounge. She smiled at Edward.

"Sorry about that."

She laughed. "No. But I would quite like dinner with you, Edward."

"Great!" He laughed quietly then, shaking his head. "That's a relief. I won't lie, Jac, I was afraid you'd say no."

"Well there's nothing wrong with a little white lie sometimes, Edward. I've probably told a few myself. As have other people. As long as something good comes out of it, I don't see the harm. Do you?"

Edward grinned and pulled her towards him. "No harm at all." MW

ACT OF KINDNESS

In hospital with my child during her heart surgery, my husband and 3 other children stayed at home. Without a word, my neighbour arrived each morning to collect the washing and ironing.

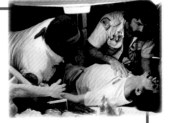

✦ In 1998, larger than life hero Bruce Willis burst onto the screen to save the planet from a massive meteor in *Armageddon.*

✦ Stanley Kubrick's 1968 movie, *2001: Space Odyssey* is now iconic, the HAL 9000 computer is a character in its own right, and the movie pioneered numerous special effects.

✦ *The Martian* (2015) combined nail-biting drama with scientific ingenuity as Matt Damon hogged the screen time in the role of Mark Watney, stranded on Mars and trying to stay alive.

✦ *First Man* was released in 2018 to coincide with the 50th anniversary of the Moon landings, starring Ryan Gosling as Neil Armstrong. The landing sequence is simply beautiful cinema.

FANCY THAT!

Fascinating facts on **Space Movies!**

✦ *Alien* in 1979 starred Sigourney Weaver as perhaps the first kick-ass female lead character. The horror on the actors' faces during the famous chest bursting scene was real as they didn't know it was coming!

✦ George Clooney stars in the 2002 remake of *Solaris*, a movie that questions what is real and what is not, and makes you wonder if we should even go out into space at all!

✦ *The Day the Earth Stood Still* in 1951 is a classic what-if-aliens-landed story, in which chaos follows the appearance of Michael Rennie and his robot!

✦ In 1997, *Event Horizon* blurred the lines between a space movie and a horror movie as its crew gets picked off one by one, leading to an ending full of blood and gore!

✦ Strictly speaking not a space movie, but 1982's classic *E.T.* is an iconic family adventure that had a real feel-good factor and plenty Kleenex moments.

Apollo 13, released in 1995, is a portrayal of the failed mission to the Moon in 1970

The Brewery Horses

Justin wanted to be modern, but Clare knew some traditions were worth more than money

By Julia Douglas

S tamford's Brewery was one of the city's landmarks. Its central spire-like chimney could be seen from miles around and its beery aroma of hops and yeast could be smelt far and wide.

Several major routes converged on the road that encircled the premises, meaning that a parade of red buses, black taxis, cars and lorries revolved around it day and night.

Behind the tall red-brick wall, though, lay a sunny oasis of calm and a scene unchanged in a century.

"Good boy, Hercules."

Clare enjoyed the sense of peace as she gave the gleaming white Shire horse's flank a final brush. The animal was huge; she couldn't even see over his back. His head towered above her, his plaited mane decorated with a row of scarlet bows against the clear blue sky.

"Come on, boy."

The solid ton of horse snorted but responded obediently as the slender, blonde 20-year-old reached up to his bridle and led him clip-clopping in a slow circle around the stableyard.

Samson, the horse's twin, was already standing in front of the brewery dray, held by Alf, the burly, grey-haired drayman, resplendent in red hunting jacket, black bowtie and black bowler hat. ➜

The wagon was loaded with shiny metal beer barrels.

"Back up, Hercules."

Clare held the horse's nose in both hands to guide him as he stepped backwards into position beside Samson. His big hooves were shrouded in the breed's distinctive long ankle hair that made him look as though he were wearing flared trousers.

"Good boy."

Clare patted the gentle giant as Alf lowered the dray's shafts to either side of the team. They'd just secured the shiny chains between horses and cart when a sleek red Ford Capri swung through the open wooden gates and parked by the back door of the offices.

"Here he comes," Alf muttered, darkly. "Our new boss. Look at him. Fresh out of university. What does he know about runnin' a brewery?"

Clare was looking all right, keen to get her first proper look at Justin Stamford, the great-great-grandson of the brewery's founder, who all the girls in the company had been excitedly discussing for the past fortnight. He was certainly eye-catching, with his long, wavy blond hair that shone like gold in the morning sun, flared brown suit and wide aquamarine tie.

"I'm glad I'm retirin' next month," Alf grumbled as he levered himself onto the dray's tall steel-rimmed wheel and from there to its lofty seat. "Walk on."

Justin stood by his car with an armful of files, watching the dray as it paused in the gateway, waiting for a gap in the busy traffic outside.

To Clare's surprise, he turned and smiled at her. A twinkle in his blue eyes made her feel suddenly self-conscious in her navy-blue jumper that was covered in white horse hairs, and riding boots covered in worse.

"Quite a sight, eh?" Justin indicated the departing dray. "It will almost be a shame to see the horses go."

"Go?" Clare yelped, startled.

"Ah, sorry. You don't know yet, do you?" Justin walked over, looking contrite. "I suppose I might as well be the one to tell you. When Alf retires next month, we're retiring the horses, too. We'll be delivering by lorry from now on."

Clare felt as if a trapdoor had opened in the flagstones beneath her.

"You can't get rid of the horses!" she blurted. "They're the brewery's symbol."

She pointed helplessly at the wrought iron Shire horse atop the words *Stamford's Brewery* that stood in an wide arch astride the big gates.

"They'll still be on the bottle labels." Justin grinned.

"But…" Clare desperately searched for an argument. "The horses have been delivering to pubs around the city for a hundred years."

"Exactly! It's the 1970s, not the 1870s, and times have changed. Look at that traffic. It's no place for a horse and cart. Then there's the cost."

The young business graduate gazed around the yard's buildings as he said, "Apart from the price of feed, there are you grooms, the tack makers… we even have our own blacksmith."

"He's a farrier," Clare couldn't help correcting him.

"Well, whatever he is, we can replace the whole operation with just one man and a truck. But don't worry," he smiled kindly. "We'll find you another job in the brewery. Now, if you'll excuse me, I'm due in the boardroom."

Clare watched him walk away and felt like he'd taken her whole life from her.

Clare was a city girl through and through. She was 10-years-old before she caught her first glimpse of the countryside and she hadn't liked it much – it was far too green and quiet – but she'd loved horses all her life.

One of her earliest memories was the clip-clop of hooves and the rattle of cart wheels as the rag and bone man pulled into her street of council houses, when she was about five-years-old.

"Rag, bo' lum-bah!" the totter had

mum felt embarrassed going up to the desk sergeant, but the ruddy faced policeman always rolled his eyes indulgently and agreed to them taking a peek at the horses in the stable at the back of the building.

It was in that long, light and airy shed, as she walked between the rows of straw-strewn stalls that she fell in love with the smell of hay and horses. Somehow, even as a girl, she'd felt at home there.

Clare's favourite horses, though, had always been the Stamford's drays. Waiting patiently outside the Bell, eating from their nosebags or drinking from a pail of water while the drayman and publican manhandled barrels through the trapdoor in the pavement, the magnificent white Shires dwarfed even the police horses.

Clare watched him walk away and felt as if he'd taken her whole life from her

called while his longhaired black and white nag whinnied.

While other residents manhandled old baths and mangles into the scrapman's cart, Clare had begged her mum for a carrot or a sugar lump to feed the horse. She loved the wet lick of its tongue as it took the treat from her palm and the rough hairy feel of its nose as she patted the snorting animal.

"His name's Trigger," said the bearded totter who was wearing fingerless gloves, a tailcoat and a top hat that looked like it had been pulled from a dustbin.

The horse didn't look much like his big screen namesake, but Clare felt like Roy Rogers when the totter lifted her onto the animal's sagging back.

On shopping trips to the high street, Clare always pleaded with her mother for a visit to the police station. She knew her

In her last year at school, Clare had written to the brewery asking for a job and been over the moon when they took her on as a groom. Her dream was to one day drive a dray, but in a single conversation Justin had dashed that hope forever.

"Come on, boy."

With the familiar smell of hops in her nose, Clare led Hercules around the sunny yard for exercise.

Instinctively, he pulled towards the empty dray parked beside the silent forge.

"Sorry, Hercules," Clare turned him gently away from the cart. "You're not going out today."

The company had always used a fleet of articulated lorries to deliver nationwide, but she'd never thought she'd see the day when a small lorry would take over the rounds of local pubs.

Dejected, she led Hercules to the ➜

stable where Samson was the only other horse left and she was the last member of the equine staff – although she wouldn't be for long.

Clare wondered what it was going to be like wearing a white coat and hairnet in the yeasty vat room with Josie, her former fellow groom. She was grateful that Justin had found her another job, but it wasn't the one she'd spent her childhood dreaming of.

She wondered if she'd see much of Justin on the brewery floor, and why that even mattered to her. Alf was right: he was just a spoilt rich boy who knew nothing about running a brewery. She shouldn't keep thinking about him.

"Ah, Clare, good news!"

Justin's flares flapped and his blond glasses flopped an ample bosom over the sill of a first floor window and shouted across the yard.

"Ron's just called from a phonebox. Your new lorry's broken down and he reckons it'll need a tow to the garage!"

"I don't believe it!" Justin exclaimed. "All our other lorries are out. How will we get the beer delivered now?"

"We've still got Hercules and Samson," Clare pointed out.

"Yes, but we don't have a drayman now Alf's retired." Justin gripped his chin in anguish.

"I'll drive," Clare offered.

"Can you, really?" He looked at her with an eager expression that made something flip inside her.

"Yes – I may never get another chance," she grinned.

She felt like she was sitting on top of the world as she sat in the drayman's seat

locks bounced on the breeze as he strode across the yard in a royal-blue three-piece suit and matching tie. "I've finally found a good home for Hercules and Samson. A nice little farm up the country, with plenty of grass to eat and no more carts to pull. How do you like the sound of that, Samson?" he said.

"This is Hercules," Clare corrected, testily. "And I don't think he'd like the countryside, he's a town horse. Besides, he's not ready to retire. He's in his prime."

"You'll be able to visit him." Justin jerked a thumb towards his Capri and added in a hopeful tone, "I could drive you, if you like."

The prospect of a car trip with Justin caught Clare's interest in spite of herself.

"Mr Justin!"

A matronly secretary with a grey beehive and sharp-cornered cat's eye

"I'd better come with you," said Justin, "to help you unload the barrels."

She looked at his smart suit and her horse-hair-covered jumper.

"First, we'd better look the part. Hold Hercules for a mo'," she said.

Leaving the bemused manager with the rein, Clare dashed into the tack room. She returned with a new red hunting jacket buttoned over a white blouse, and a bowler hat on her head.

"Wow." Justin looked her up and down in a way that sent tingles up her neck.

Blushing, she pushed Alf's jacket into Justin's arms and stood on tiptoe to plonk a bowler atop his thick blond waves.

"Musn't let the brewery's image down," she winked. "Now let's get the horses hooked up."

Clare felt like she was sitting on top of the world as she bounced along on the drayman's seat, high above the giant white Shire horses. Towering over taxis, cars, cyclists and pedestrians, it was like riding the top deck of a bus, only in the open air. With a fresh breeze in her face, the gold and brown leaves of overhanging trees almost brushed her bowler as they trotted along the road.

A motorbike screamed past them, far too close, and Clare flinched. Hercules and Samson, wearing leather blinkers emblazoned with the company's symbol, didn't even twitch.

"I can't believe they're so calm in all this traffic," Justin marvelled as he stood close behind her, gripping the iron frame of her seat.

"It's the life they know." Clare grinned, and began to relax. "They know the route so well I hardly even have to steer."

As they'd left the brewery gates, her stomach had been in her throat and her heart had drummed in her ears. She hadn't known how she was going to maneuver a horse and cart into such fast-moving traffic.

A bus driver had slowed to let her out, however, and even given her a deferential salute. When she held out her crop to change lanes, a taxi driver was similarly accommodating.

"They're treating us like royalty," Justin grinned as he thanked the cabbie with a wave.

"The Stamford's horses are symbols of the city," Clare said proudly. "Look how pleased everyone is to see us."

She touched the brim of her bowler to acknowledge the waves of a young housewife and her grinning gap-toothed children.

Later that afternoon, Justin was stripped down to his rolled shirt sleeves. Clare rolled a barrel to the end of the dray and he lifted it down to the pavement with a loud grunt.

Looking down at him while she caught her breath, she reckoned the hard work agreed with him. He'd always looked dishy in a suit and tie, but with a few shirt buttons undone and a gleam of sweat on his brow he was even more attractive.

"That's the lot, then," said a red-scalped publican with a bushy moustache as he emerged from the pavement trapdoor to sign the delivery slip. "What 'appened to your new lorry?"

"It broke down," Justin admitted sheepishly.

The publican gave a derisive snort and prodded Justin in the chest with a sausage-like finger.

"Well, when you get back, young man, you can tell your boss he's a fool for taking these beautiful horses off the street. Part of history they are. They're the soul of this city."

"That's right, young man." Clare leaned over the side of the dray, at Justin's shoulder. "You be sure to tell him," she said wryly.

When Justin burst out laughing, she did, too.

"I've really enjoyed today," said Justin, when they got back to the yard.

"So have I."

Clare accepted his gallantly offered hand to steady her as she jumped ➡

down from the dray's steel-rimmed wheel.

"How did you learn to drive so well?" he asked.

"Alf was teaching me. I hoped – well, I'm afraid I assumed – that when he retired I'd take over. I even bought myself the jacket."

"I thought it fitted rather well." Justin eyed her pinched waist.

"At least I got to wear it for a day." Clare turned and dashed away a tear as she realised that was all the outing had been – a one day reprieve for the horses, or perhaps a day or two at the most, while the lorry was repaired.

She suddenly regretted getting so friendly with Justin when he was the man who was taking all this away from her.

"Actually, today has made me realise I was wrong to bring in the lorry," Justin

"Good boy, Hercules. It's nearly time to go."

He scratched the giant animal's neck, picked up the water pail and hung it under the dray. Then he looked up, not at a pub, but at a big, grey city church as the bells in the tower began to peal merrily.

The arched doors opened and Justin spilled out in his long-tailed morning suit and top hat, with Clare in her beautiful

She dashed away a tear as she realised this had just been a one day reprieve

said quietly. "The horses are ambassadors for the company and I'm going to reinstate them – and with you in charge of the operation."

"Do you mean that?" Clare beamed.

"You've shown me that there's so much more to running a brewery than the balance sheet."

"Oh, Justin, I could kiss you!"

Clare clapped her hands over her mouth and blushed to her roots as she realised what she'd said – and to her boss of all people!

Justin's eyes were twinkling. "Don't let me stop you," he smiled, invitingly.

A year later, Alf was back at the kerbside with his favourite horses. Retirement had given him a paunch but his red hunting jacket still did up – well, just about.

white gown by his side. Confetti and good wishes swirled around them.

Alf positioned a set of wooden steps at the rear of the dray and Justin gallantly handed his beautiful new wife aboard, along with Josie, her maid of honour, some bridesmaids and the couples' parents, all dressed in their finest.

The brewery's entire staff cheered from the pavement as Justin and Clare clinked their beer glasses. Then the giant Shire horses trotted forward, taking the happy couple to their future. **MW**

Brain Boosters

Missing Link

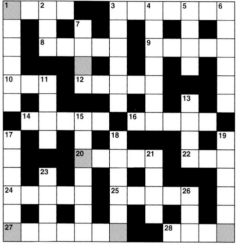

The answer to each clue is a word which has a link with each of the three words listed. This word may come at the end (eg HEAD linked with BEACH, BIG, HAMMER), at the beginning (eg BLACK linked with BEAUTY, BOARD and JACK) or a mixture of the two (eg STONE linked with HAIL, LIME and WALL).

ACROSS

1 Busy, Clock, Guard (4)
3 Battery, High, Solar (7)
8 Collar, Egg, Lie (5)
9 Get, Play, Side (5)
10 Dustbin, Eye, Saucepan (3)
12 Irrigation, Last, Water (5)
14 Good, Lost, Way (5)
16 Butter, Soda, Sour (5)
20 Dog, Home, Occupier (5)
22 Down, Dutch, Plymouth (3)
24 High, Jester, Squash (5)
25 Mass, Mixed, Studies (5)
27 Arts, Democrat, Party (7)
28 Camp, Red, Salvation (4)

DOWN

1 Field, Lines, Pitched (6)
2 Drop, Point, Pond (3)
3 Much, Penny, Sitting (6)
4 Board, Forecast, Vane (7)
5 Beer, Square, Tap (4)
6 Gold, Grave, Mechanical (6)
7 Brain, Humming, Table (4)
11 Bridge, Prize, String (4)
13 Cycle, Foot, War (4)
15 Pea, Sharp, Six (7)
17 Food, Force, Post (6)
18 Magnetism, Rights, Wild (6)
19 Queen, Sleep, Spot (6)
21 Awakening, Health, Joke (4)
23 Bell, Struck, Waiter (4)
26 Craft, Fresh, Tight (3)

Turn To Page 159 For Solutions

Hidden word in the shaded squares: _____

A Chance To Grow

Anna was a florist and knew a thing or two about giving growing things the space they needed to flourish

By Tess Niland Kimber

"Milly's gone!" Tony gasped down the phone.

"Not again!" Anna said, alarmed. She tucked her phone under her chin. Her mobile had rung as she was finishing her latest floral display. When she saw the call was from her husband Tony, she'd feared his fifteen-year old daughter was in trouble again. It was the only time he phoned her at work.

"The school rang – after contacting Fiona," he explained. Fear trimmed his voice and she longed to be with him, to hold him, comfort him. "Or rather tried contacting Fi. She's in Andalucia with her latest boyfriend."

Anna rarely criticised Tony's ex-wife although she quietly believed Fi was part of Milly's problems. Since Tony and Fi divorced four years ago, she'd had a succession of boyfriends, none of whom had lasted. The constant stream of possible new "fathers" must unsettle Milly. No wonder she ran away. So far, they'd always found her but each time she fled it terrified Anna and Tony.

Milly was a lovely girl and Anna was very fond of her. Why couldn't Fi appreciate her lovely daughter? She bit her tongue. Right now, the last thing Tony needed was her complaining about his ex-wife.

"When did Milly go this time?" She willed her fingers to work quickly as she

Anna was fond of Milly but her habit of running away was stressing Tony out

"You mean, Fi left Milly alone in the house? Why didn't she say she was on holiday? Milly could have stayed with us."

"No idea – I'm as shocked as you. Fi'll never win Mother of the Year but leaving our daughter home alone is her worst move so far."

"Well, when we find her this time she must stay with us. Milly shouldn't be alone. What was Fi thinking?"

pushed carnations into the foam oasis. Once this display was finished, she'd lock up the shop and look for Milly.

"The school isn't sure. She missed registration so they phoned the house and then Fi's mobile. Apparently, she wasn't happy when they tracked her down."

"Is she worried about Milly?" For once, Anna sympathised with Fi.

How frightening it must be to discover

your daughter was missing again when you were hundreds – maybe even thousands, her geography wasn't that hot! – of miles away. But her sympathy was short-lived.

"No, Fi moaned at the Head for phoning her in Spain. Apparently, her mobile charges are huge and she'll be billed for receiving the call."

"Unbelievable!" she breathed.

Normally, she avoided passing judgment on Tony's ex – she didn't think it was very constructive, especially if Milly was around – but sometimes it was hard not to. Fi's parenting was very "relaxed".

"Look, I'll watch out for Milly along the High Street. Keep trying her mobile. Have you called the police?"

"The school did, explaining it's not the first time she's run off."

"It's not even the first time this   ➤

month!" she said, glancing around the shop and deciding her next job should be tidying the yellow roses and lilies in buckets by the front door. But that task would have to wait. She must find Milly first.

"Right – I'll phone if there's any news. See you later at the flat."

"Course. Try not worry, Tony, though it's hard, I know."

After ending the call, Anna returned her attention to the large floral display. Working quickly, she trimmed some pink peonies and red dahlias. This commission from the local council was her best yet. Hopefully, it would lead to more work from them. She needed some regular contracts so her new business could keep up with the competition. But right now Pink Petals was the least of her worries. She had to find her step-daughter.

Milly was a lovely girl but didn't cope well with pressure. Her only solution was to run away. Not that Anna blamed her. Life was tough at fifteen. No, scratch that – life could be hard at any age, she thought, but few situations were improved by running away from them.

"I can't help it, Anna. When I'm stressed, I do a runner," Milly had explained the last time she'd disappeared.

"But it's dangerous. You don't know…" She didn't want to scare her but needed to warn her, "…who's about. Don't run next time. Talk to someone. Talk to us."

Milly had shrugged her shoulders and tried to look tough. "I'll be all right."

Anna had smiled tightly at the tiny fifteen-year old. Even with lashings of eyeliner, a lip piercing and spiky, dyed red hair she still looked vulnerable.

"She's a good kid," Tony often praised.

"Yes, she is. She's just finds change hard to cope with. If only we could offer her a home, or at least share custody with Fi to ease the pressure," Anna would whisper, laid in his arms at night.

"It would be good but we couldn't even house a kitten, here."

He was right. The flat had been his bachelor pad after his divorce. It had one bedroom, a small fitted kitchen and a cosy lounge that looked over the college sports field. She loved it but it was cramped. If it was bigger, Milly could stay with them more often. After their wedding, they'd planned to move but when the chance came up for Anna to take over the High Street's florist, they'd put their savings into Pink Petals, instead.

"It's an investment. Once you start making money we'll save for a deposit on a bigger place," Tony had argued. "Then we can offer Milly a home – if she wants."

There was a bedsit above the shop but it was smaller than their flat so they couldn't move into that. Tony planned to paint it for her so she could rent it out, giving them more income. Buying the business instead of a new house made financial sense but that was before Milly had started to run away.

The displays were almost ready for the council who were entertaining some visiting dignitaries and decorating the conference suite with fresh flowers. Busy as she was, Anna's mind was on Milly and where she might be. Even as she worked, she checked her mobile dozens of times in case Milly had contacted her.

Over the last year, Milly had run away several times but had always been found, either at friends' houses, the shopping mall, the park – and, once, down by the canal. There wasn't a pattern; she wound up somewhere new every time.

Creamy clematis added finishing touches to the displays. Pleased with her work, Anna wondered if there was time for a cuppa before delivering the flowers. No, she decided, if she wanted time to search for Milly en route then she'd have to settle for a quick glass of water from the kitchenette at the back of the shop. Over

she'd opted not to try to replace her mother but to be a friend to her, instead. So far, it had worked. "So," Anna said, reaching for two mugs, "what happened?" She didn't add, "this time."

Milly sighed. "Everything got on top of me. I've got coursework coming out my ears. Mum's got a new boyfriend I can't stand. She left me to go to Spain with him."

"So, you're alone in the house?"

"Yes, but I like it. I can cook what I want and I've taught myself to use the washing machine. Last night I even vacuumed the lounge."

"Steady on!" Anna joked. "Seriously, stay with us when Mum's not... about."

Milly shrugged but Anna saw her eyes brighten. "Ah thanks, Anna... Actually, I had a problem this morning. I switched on

Poor Milly looked cold and tired with a distracted look in her sad blue eyes

the sink was a window, looking onto a brick patio where she'd hope to take her breaks in the warmer weather. Filling her glass, she thought she saw a movement. Puzzled, she went outside.

"Milly! What you doing here?"

Her step daughter, looking pale and tired, was huddled by the back wall.

"How did you get in?"

"Climbed over the wall," she said.

"Oh, be careful. Dad'll go mad if you hurt yourself."

"It's not that high..."

"Come on," Anna smiled, feeling dizzy with relief. "I'll put on the kettle. You look like you need a hot drink."

Standing together in the kitchenette, she resisted the temptation to interrogate Milly. She looked cold and tired with a distracted look in her blue eyes. Sadly, Anna didn't have her own children and sometimes felt a novice around Milly. However, early on,

the lights and they blew. I don't know what to do. Mum'll go mad."

"Why didn't you phone Dad? He'd help."

"I didn't want to bother him. Besides, Mum's a bit weird about Dad being in the house since the divorce."

The kettle clicked as it came to the boil.

"So, you did another runner?" Milly nodded. "You can't keep doing this, love," she said, quietly, reaching for her hand.

"I know," Milly squeezed her fingers.

"Right – first things first. Sorting the lights is easy. We need to replace the fuse wire. If Mum's not keen on Tony or me fixing it, I'll ring Mo. He's my odd job man for the shop. He's very reliable and lives just up the road from you."

"Really? You'd do that for me?"

"Of course," she said, handing her a mug of coffee. "We're family, aren't we?"

Milly nodded and smiled.

"As for the coursework..." ➡

"There's tons," Milly sighed, looking the image of Tony.

"Make a pile and work through it. I do that with the shop's accounts," she stirred her coffee. "You'll feel much better once you make a start. If you're really behind, we'll talk to the school. But if you never start, you'll never finish."

"Duh! I know that," she grinned.

"Stay at the flat with us – 'til Mum comes home. We'll have a Chinese tonight. Bring your work with you. Either me or Dad'll help you."

"Duh – I want to pass the course!"

"Cheeky!" Anna laughed.

you can't leg it every time something doesn't go your way. It's scary. If not for you then for us."

"Sorry – it's just I'm so fed up at home. Mum does her best, but…"

Anna tried not to look doubtful.

"I know she's keen to find someone new before she gets too old but most of her blokes have been awful. I can't wait to leave home and go to college."

"That's a solution, certainly, but you'll have sixth form, first."

"I know – it'll take ages."

Tony sighed. "Anna and I are saving to buy a bigger

"I have an idea to give Milly the space she needs," said Anna

After phoning Tony, the school, the police, and texting Fi to report she was safe, Anna and Milly drove to the council's offices to deliver the flowers. She was quietly impressed with Milly's good manners when the receptionist showed them through to the conference suite to arrange the displays.

Then Anna drove Milly home, waiting outside while she packed a few things and collected her schoolwork.

Once back at the flat, Milly lay on the lounge floor and started ploughing through her course work.

"Tackle some easy pieces, first, then you'll already have a smaller pile."

"Good idea," Milly said, holding a pen between her teeth.

Tony came in at six. "So, you've shown up again, young lady…"

"Tony, Milly's explained…" Anna shot him a glance, warning him a telling off was probably misplaced.

He sighed and then crouched beside his daughter, giving her a hug. "Look, I know things are a bit mental at the moment, but

place, then if you want to and Mum agrees, you can live with us. But it'll take time and there's one condition – no more running away."

"Wouldn't need to then, would I?" Milly grinned.

After eating the takeaway, Milly offered to wash up.

"Good job, I'm sitting down!" Tony laughed.

Once she was in the kitchen, he whispered to Anna, "What are we going to do? She can't stay here indefinitely."

"No… I've an idea, though. It might not work but…"

Tony and Anna decided not to tell Milly their plans until they'd completed some work. The following weekend they bought some white emulsion and painted the small bedsit above the shop. Tony also fixed a couple of the kitchen cupboards and changed a bathroom tap washer.

"Doesn't look half bad, even if I say so myself," he said, curling his arms around Anna. "It's not quite one of those gorgeous properties from "Grand Designs," but it's a big improvement. Think Milly will like it?"

"There's only one way to find out – let's ask her."

Anna wouldn't admit it but, even without the offer of the bedsit, she was quietly confident Milly wouldn't run away again. She'd tackled a lot of her coursework and last night at the flat, she'd looked happier than she had for some months.

"Mum's coming home tomorrow afternoon," Milly told Anna.

"Bit early, isn't it? I thought they weren't flying back until next week."

"The boyfriend – or rather ex-boyfriend – isn't. But Mum's swapped her flight for an earlier one."

"Trouble in paradise?"

"Could say that," Milly said, jumping up to sit on the worktop, "Seems the new boyfriend couldn't stop ogling girls on the beach and, if that wasn't bad enough, Mum found him in a clinch with one of the waitresses."

"Not good, then."

She says it put her off men for a while."

"Mightn't be a bad thing… Anyway, your Dad and I have a surprise for you."

"For me?"

"Yes – if your Mum agrees. How about using the bedsit as a bolt hole? Every time you feel like running away – don't. Instead, go and chill in the bedsit."

"Really?" Her face lit up.

"We've been decorating. It's not exactly a palace but it'll give you a bit of space. And it means you won't need to run away."

Milly looked stunned. Her blue eyes filled with tears. "You did all that for me?"

"Of course," Anna said. "You need a place to go when things get on top of you. We can't offer you a permanent home just yet. This feels like the next best thing."

She sprung off the side into her arms,

hugging her. "Thank you! Thank you, both!" she cried.

Strangely, Milly never did run away again. Oh, she often wound up at the bedsit where she'd watch a film or use the time and space to plough through her coursework, but she didn't run off. She seemed more settled at home, too. Anna was quietly confident Milly's disappearing days were behind her.

"I don't get it," Tony had said, pushing a hand through his dark hair. "How does the bedsit make such a difference?"

"I think Milly likes knowing there's always somewhere to go if things became unbearable again."

"Like a safety net?" Anna nodded. "Do you mind that we can't rent out the bedsit over the florists while Milly wants to use it?" he asked.

"No," she smiled. "It made you paint it and besides, we'll soon get a tenant when Milly no longer needs it."

"I'm just so pleased she's stopped running away every time she comes unstuck," Tony said. "And Fi being home more has helped, too."

"Sometimes, the solution isn't finding the answer. It's just knowing one exists."

Tony pulled her to him. "Pretty good at this step-parenting business, aren't you?"

"I wouldn't go that far but it's working for Milly. That's the main thing."

Kids were like flowers, really, she thought. Both just needed space and their chance to grow… **MW**

ACT OF KINDNESS

When our twins were in Special Care we came home from another gruelling day to find a beautiful fruit cake in our porch from our friend Mo to encourage us to eat. I've never forgotten her kindness.

An Easter Surprise

After five years there'd been no sign of a proposal, and Kylie was beginning to lose hope of it ever happening…

By Rosemary Hayes

"Surprise!" Nathan called out. Kylie rolled over in bed to see her boyfriend standing there with a tray. She didn't know what looked better, his bare chest, or the plate of toasted hot cross buns.

"What's all this?" she said, as she adjusted her pillows to sit up.

"Breakfast in bed, of course," said Nathan. "Hope you like your Easter buns dripping with lots of butter."

"That's one of my favourite things about Easter," she said, as Nathan put the tray on her lap. Buns, coffee, fresh fruit, a posy of flowers, how lovely… her mother often asked why she stayed with Nathan when after five years it still looked like there

used to organise the most wonderful egg hunts when we were growing up. All my cousins would be there and we would run around her backyard like whirlwinds. We'd find eggs in bushes, and in her peg basket, in pockets of clothes hanging from the clothes line, all through the cubby house, inside these cuplike flowers in her garden, some were just scattered over the ground for the younger kids to find easily and pick up."

"I bet you always collected the most."

"Not always. Besides, after the hunt all the eggs would go in one pile and then they would be shared out evenly. I always hinted I didn't mind getting more of the white chocolate ones, since they were my favourite. The funny thing is, we always found old eggs missed from the year before,

"Thank you so much, that brought back great memories of Gran's Easters"

wasn't a proposal in sight, sometimes she even wondered herself, but then he would do something thoughtful like this. "Thank you. Did I ever tell you my Gran made her own hot cross buns? I still remember how delicious they were. That was almost my favourite thing about Easter."

"Almost? What was the best thing?"

"Easter egg hunts," she smiled wistfully. "I'm sure I've told you before. My Gran

and my cousin Trent would eat them!"

"Sounds like you have really great memories of Easter."

"I do," she agreed. "It's just a shame that somewhere along the line we got too old for Easter Egg hunts."

"Have we? I'm not so sure about that." Nathan reached beside the bed and then put in her hands an empty cane basket.

"You organised an Easter egg hunt for

me? I love you!" she grinned.

"I sure hope so," Nathan said, as Kylie slipped on her shoes and headed out the back.

For the next half an hour Kylie felt like a little girl again as she darted around the backyard searching for eggs. The basket was filling quickly. There were eggs of all different sizes. Some were solid, some hollow. All were wrapped in brightly coloured foil.

Nathan stayed by her side the whole time giving "warmer" and "colder" hints about where some of the harder to find ones were. Except for when he answered a phone that kept him distracted for about ten minutes.

When he got off the phone Kylie hugged him tightly. "Thank you so much, that was so much fun. It brought back great memories of Gran's Easters."

"I'm glad, but you're not finished yet, he said peering into her basket. There's still one egg to find. Over near the shed."

"Oh, OK." She headed back there and searched again. "There's nothing here."

"There has to be." Nathan searched himself. "Where is it? I definitely put it here."

"It's OK. One less egg doesn't matter."

"You don't understand," his voice filled with panic. "I prepared a hollow egg as an extra special surprise for you. One wrapped in gold foil."

"Oh, I found that one while you were on the phone, the foil had come apart a bit and had ants crawling all over it, so I threw it in the bin."

"Okay, I'll just fish it out of the bin."

"No, not the kitchen bin… the outside bin," she said as he headed to the house. "But I have plenty of chocolate already."

"It's not just any egg," he wailed. "It has an engagement ring inside."

Before Kylie could say a word they both heard a familiar noise, one they heard every Monday morning. They stared at each other wide-eyed, then both turned and tried to out-sprint the approaching garbage truck. **MW**

....

GREAT READS

Why not try our Pocket Novel series, out every fortnight? You'll get a full-length romantic story for just £3.99.

Let In The Light

In the hands of a sympathetic restorer, even the most faded colours can glow once more…

By Della Galton

YEAR ONE

The group had paused in a wood panelled room that smelled of lilies and old books to look at the stained glass windows. I paused too. I'd always had a thing about glass and these windows were breathtaking, backlit by the morning sun and clearly from another age. "A gentler age," my Aunt Maud would have said.

The windows were a montage of simply outlined blooms with petals drawn in delicate colours: lemon, pale blue and a dull red. I wondered if they had always been that colour, or whether the glass had faded over time from

He was tall, gentle-voiced, his dark good looks marred by a slightly bulbous nose. Not that I was in the market for good looks.

I smiled at him. Then I looked pointedly away.

Handsome is as handsome does. That was another one of Aunt Maud's sayings. Every family has a wise matriarch, doesn't it, and Aunt Maud was ours.

She'd been right about that too; at least as far as Henry was concerned.

There was nothing original about Henry's defection. It could be summed up as *Handsome husband leaves middle-aged wife for younger model.*

Isobel, his younger model, was just a few years older than our youngest

Henry had rediscovered himself through the rose-tinted glasses of Isobel

many years of exposure to the sun.

Manston House, which was owned by the National Trust, was a little like that. Faded grandeur. Once new and beautiful, but now shabby, its glory days long gone.

Oh gosh, I knew how that felt.

"They're Edwardian," the tour guide's voice broke into my thoughts. "Naturalistic free-form, from the arts and crafts period. Think William Morris."

daughter. She worked in the mirror shop across the road from Henry's office.

Mirror, mirror on the wall, who is the fairest of them all? Not me, it seemed, when it all came out.

Henry blamed late nights, pressures of work, being made redundant and rediscovering himself through the rose tinted glasses of someone who told him he was handsome on a regular basis. Men's

looks fade in a different way to women's.

It was tough that first year. The despair, the divorce, the dividing of property. I felt like brittle glass myself. Fragile and capable of being shattered by the slightest touch.

YEAR TWO

"One door closes, another opens," Aunt Maud told me. She had outlived both my parents but the truth was, we had always been closer than the aunt/niece relationship often is because I had far more in common with her than I'd ever had with them.

Mum had been a solicitor, Dad an accountant. Aunt Maud was an artist like me. Some of my best and earliest memories are of going to her house, which smelled of turps and paint and freshly baked loaves because she had a breadmaker permanently on the go.

She would be in oversized overalls standing at a canvas, her long dark hair tied back in a butterfly clip and more often than not with a blob of blue or ➥

green paint on her nose. Seascapes were her speciality.

Aunt Maud had been married twice. She had divorced her first husband but the latter one, Jeremiah, had died. She said she was in no hurry to find a replacement, partly because Jeremiah had been her soulmate and partly because she had another lover – her art.

It was Aunt Maud who inspired me to run back into the arms of art too, rather than to hit the dating scene again, which was what many of my friends in similar situations were doing.

There had been a time when I'd planned to make art my career as Aunt Maud had done. I'd just completed a Fine Arts degree when I'd fallen pregnant with Sarah and married Henry.

I'd never done anything with my degree. Partly thanks to the distractions of having four daughters, partly because of laziness and partly, I think, because of lack of confidence. As the time had gone on it had become harder, but it was easier than I expected to update my skills and with Aunt Maud's encouragement I got a part-time job as a relief curator in our local museum.

In my spare time I went back to college. I'd always planned to specialise in glass and so I began to work with stained glass.

I made lightshades and porch art and sun catchers for friends and family and was eventually persuaded by Sarah, the only one of my daughters who still lived close by, to sell them on eBay where to my surprise I found an enthusiastic customer base.

It was towards the middle of the second year that I met Alan. We met through eBay, as it happened, when he got in touch with a proposition.

This turned out to be helping out on a restoration project of some windows at an old school. Alan and his wife, Eleanor, worked with glass too. That first project led on to other things, one of which was to be part of a much bigger project working on houses for the National Trust.

YEAR THREE

And so I came full circle and ended up once more at Manston House, working on the William Morris-style windows I had once so much admired.

Remember the tour guide with the

bulbous nose? Not that I know him as "the tour guide" now. His name is Simon and he's Alan's older brother.

Bulbous noses run in the family, by the way: as does a passion for restoration. Being a tour guide was just a hobby for Simon. His day job lies in the restoration field too. He transforms antique furniture.

"My grandad got me into wood," he told me the first time we had lunch together. "He was a carpenter and he had this huge shed where he used to work. It was full of wood chippings and sawdust and it smelled amazing."

I leaned forward to listen, warmed by the nostalgic delight on his face.

Lunch is maybe over-egging it a bit. We were at Manston House and we were sitting on a wooden bench by the

"That's my Aunt Maud all right," I told him proudly.

Soon after Aunt Maud gave him the official seal of approval, Simon did something very old-fashioned and charming. He asked her if she would object to the idea of him being her nephew-in-law.

I had an inkling of this already because we had been to an antiques fair the week before and Simon had lingered beside a jewellery stall that sold beautiful vintage rings with precious stones set in clawed settings. He caught my hand and drew me closer.

"Which would you choose?" he had asked me, as we looked at a tray of diamond rings that glinted brightly in the sun beneath their glass case.

When I'd looked up at him his eyes

Her blue eyes sparkled. "Bring him to tea when you're ready to share him"

lake, eating a sandwich together, in between work shifts.

We progressed over that summer to proper lunches, although they were often outside. The weather was glorious – hot blue days and sunshine – so picnics by deep green rivers and in leaf-dappled woodland glades were perfect, and we never seemed to run out of things to say.

"No sense in rushing things," Aunt Maud said when I told her about Simon. Her blue eyes sparkled. "Bring him to tea when you're ready to share him. That's if you don't think meeting an eccentric old lady will put him off!"

"What do you think?" I hugged her.

Simon loved Aunt Maud. He had in fact already heard of her.

"Maud Gilby Seascapes. She does a lot of card designs, doesn't she? Very individual style."

had held questions multi-faceted as glass.

"I mean, that's if you would choose any of them at all should the occasion demand it?"

"I would, yes. Definitely."

We smiled at each other before looking back at the glittering creations.

YEAR FOUR

Simon has taught me so much over the last couple of years about restoration. Not just of old houses, but of humans too. Humans need a different kind of restoration when they get broken, don't they? One that's about healing and learning to trust again.

Simon lost his wife Wendy a year before Henry left, so he had a head start on the recovery process, but not so much of one that he didn't remember very clearly what it was like. ➤

We talked a lot about our erstwhile partners and what went wrong and how there was fault on both sides, as there always is, and how we thought we might one day risk taking the plunge again.

And then there was that moment when we ended up at the vintage ring stall and there was that moment when Simon got on his knees and proposed.

He did that in style too. We had just been to a glass exhibition in Montreal that I'd said I would love to see, and were having lunch in an outdoor café close to St Lawrence River. He dropped the ring and it rolled within inches of an open drain cover. Once it was safely retrieved and we'd got over the shock of nearly losing it – and I'd said yes, of course – we laughed and laughed.

Simon is standing beside me now. Above our heads, sunshine pours through the beautiful stained glass windows of the sixteenth-century church. The vicar's dog collar is touched with reflected colour, as is my cream satin wedding dress. Both are lit with flickers of lemon and blue and red.

It reminds me of the flowers at Manston House, which are now fully restored to their original beauty. I feel a little like those flowers. I feel as though I've been lit from the inside out. Lit by a warmth that would have been impossible four years ago.

It's not just glass that needs a touch of loving restoration, I think, as I interlace my fingers with Simon's and listen to the vicar reciting the words of the service we have chosen. Sometimes it's people too.

Behind him in the front pew I catch Aunt Maud's eyes and she smiles. She is resplendent in a burgundy dress and hat, which is part of my primary colour scheme, and my four daughters are dressed in it too

I feel as though I have been transformed from pastel to primary. That's how learning to love Simon has made me feel. Everything looks brighter more vibrant than it did before.

Maybe not so very different from glass then, after all… MW

....

ACT OF KINDNESS

On cold winter mornings my partner puts a heater in my car (on an extension lead) and turns it round so I don't have to reverse out of the drive.

65
Calories per
biscuit

Chilli And Cheese Sables

Ingredients (Makes 36)

- ◆ **175g plain flour**
- ◆ **125g butter, diced**
- ◆ **50g Emmental cheese, finely grated**
- ◆ **75g mature Cheddar cheese, finely grated**
- ◆ **1 fresh red chilli, seeded and finely chopped**
- ◆ **1 egg, lightly beaten**
- ◆ **2tbsp each poppy seeds, sesame seeds, caraway seeds and finely chopped walnuts**
- ◆ **Sea salt to sprinkle, optional**

1 Sift the flour into a bowl and rub in the butter, until the mixture resembles fine breadcrumbs. Mix in the cheeses and chilli and press together to form a dough.

2 Gently knead on a lightly floured surface and then cut into 4. Shape each piece into a 4cm diameter log. One at a time, brush the log with beaten egg and then roll in one of the seeds or the walnuts, to coat. Place on a baking sheet lined with baking parchment, cover and chill for 1hr.

3 Preheat the oven to 180°C, Fan 160°C, Gas 4. Lightly grease 2 baking trays. Cut each log into 4-5mm slices and place, spaced apart, on the trays. Brush the tops with the remaining egg, sprinkle with a few grains of sea salt if wished, and bake for 12-15min until golden. Serve warm or cold. ➔ **97**

RECIPE AND FOOD STYLING: JENNIE SHAPTER PHOTOGRAPHY: JON WHITTAKER

A Change Of Spots

Beth and her husband David had gotten into a rut, but how could they get those old feelings back again?

By Hazel E Kendrick

O n the morning of her 45th birthday, as she had done yesterday, Beth Saunders stopped outside Ospreys Fashions. The leopard skin leggings were still in the window and Beth coveted them. She adored leopards.

Her birthday had begun with a kiss and a card from David at breakfast. His reminder, as though she needed one, that he had booked dinner at Woodlands restaurant.

Robert and Stephen had been five. David had been studying for the finals of his accountancy exams. Four days before Beth's birthday, both boys had come down with chicken pox.

"Never mind, darling," David comforted. "We'll have a feast at home. I'll pick up a Chinese and a bottle of wine." He had smiled in the way that made Beth's heart turn over. "But I want to get something special for your birthday. What would really you like?"

Beth had hesitated. There were so many

David had taken the innocent remark seriously, and the pattern was set

David always waited until evening to give Beth her present, a tradition that had begun when their twin boys were small. He was sweet and considerate, an excellent father. Beth did not want to hurt his feelings, so she did not tell him she was tired of dining at Woodlands every birthday.

Beth sighed and moved reluctantly on. As she headed for the charity shop where she volunteered, she remembered the first year David had bought her a matching underwear set for her birthday.

useful things she needed. Then she made a decision. "I'd like a special matching underwear set," she'd said.

That first set had been cream silk with a coffee lace trim. "It's perfect!" Beth had exclaimed, her eyes glowing. "I'll save it for a special occasion."

The special occasion had come six weeks later, on their seventh wedding anniversary. David had taken Beth to Woodlands, a former coaching inn – for the first time.

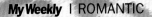

"It's perfect," Beth said again. All was right with her world. The children were better. Her mother was babysitting.

Beth leaned impulsively across the table and held David's hand. "I can't imagine anywhere nicer than this, darling," she whispered.

It had been an innocent remark. But David had taken it seriously. The pattern was set.

On her next birthday, David triumphantly handed Beth a grey and white box from Ospreys. That year the underwear had been lilac satin. The year after, a delicate peach, patterned with tiny butterflies. Underwear set after underwear set followed year by year. And so, too, did dinner at Woodlands.

As time passed, the boys grew from children to adolescents. But the ritual of the underwear sets continued. Each year a different colour.

Robert and Stephen were in their first term at university now. Beth wanted to go somewhere different for dinner. And to receive a different birthday present.

"I adore David, you know that," Beth had said to her sister Frances on the telephone yesterday. "But I don't want any more matching underwear sets! And I don't want to go to Woodlands for dinner tomorrow!"

Frances was astonished at Beth's uncharacteristic outburst.

"What do you want, then?"

"Leggings," Beth told her. "Leopardskin velvet leggings. The ones in Osprey's window display. And I want to dance the ➡

night away at Flanagan's Night Club."

Frances snorted with mirth, and reminded Beth that nobody over twenty-one went to Flanagan's, and that leopardskin velvet leggings were totally impractical.

"I don't want something practical," Beth retorted childishly.

Walking home now, Beth made a detour to avoid passing Ospreys.

Just as she got home, her mobile went. It was her mother, who now lived in a retirement flat.

"Happy birthday, darling," she said fondly. "Are you having a great day? I'm looking forward to seeing you at the weekend."

And then Beth found herself telling her mother everything.

Beth's mother chuckled. "I often wondered," she confided. "But they were all gorgeous and you always seemed thrilled. I

confessed. "I've mislaid my door key. I think I left it on the hall table. I'm still in town, so could I meet you outside Ospreys, and borrow yours?"

Guiltily she replaced the receiver.

David's office was three miles away. She pictured him leaving his desk, calling to his secretary that he wouldn't be long, hurrying to the car, parked as always in nearby Chapel Street. A creature of habit, that was David. Like the leopard, he would never change his spots.

Her suggestion of a meeting place was a touch of inspiration, and she hurried back to Ospreys to find David waiting for her, looking concerned.

"I've never known you forget your key, love," he said, handing her his. He glanced at his watch. "I'll have to get going. I have to see someone at two."

Beth went over to this window of Ospreys. "I just want a quick look in here,"

Her thoughts were gloomy... just why had his appointment been so vital?

told myself David must know best."

"They were gorgeous," Beth agreed. "But I have so many now. They have a whole deep drawer to themselves in the bedroom, most as good as new. I told David that first year that it was my idea of pure luxury. Since then, he never gets me anything else."

"He needs something to nudge him out of his rut," Beth's mother said wisely.

After saying goodbye, Beth picked up the phone again and dialled the number of David's office.

Her mother was right. It was time to give her husband a nudge.

"I've done a silly thing, darling," Beth

she called back, waiting for David to join her. But David seemed ill at ease, anxious to be off.

"I really must go!" he exclaimed. "This two o'clock appointment is vital! Sorry, darling. See you tonight."

Back home, Beth's thoughts were gloomy. She had been married to David for twenty-one years. Why on earth couldn't she tell him she wanted a different kind of birthday. And why had his two o'clock appointment been so vital?

David was later home than usual. Beth had left the door on the latch for him. The clock was striking 6.30.

"Where are you, love?" David called.

"Sitting-room," Beth called back. She had been thinking all afternoon. For years, all she had done was help at the Charity shop – and loved it – but now the boys were gone, and the days stretched out in front of her, she could retrain properly. Beth had never really liked office work, and much would have changed, but it would be worth it.

She fixed a bright smile on her face as David entered. She would tell him of her decision tonight. Over dinner at Woodlands. After he had given her that familiar grey and white box.

David entered the room carrying a covered basket. Beth stared at it.

"Surprise!" David said diffidently, his eyes unfathomable, handing it over.

"What on earth?" With fingers that fumbled, Beth lifted the lid. Found herself gazing down into the wide blue eyes of a kitten. A kitten with beautiful gold and black markings on its fur, that shone like velvet.

As Beth watched, a tiny mouth opened in a yawn. She reached out a hand and stroked the small head. The kitten began to emit a deep, rumbling purr. Beth felt tears well in her eyes and spill down her face.

"Don't you like her?" David asked anxiously.

"Oh, David, she's lovely! Beautiful!"

David's face cleared in relief. "I thought she'd be company for you. I know it's been quiet since the boys went, even though you volunteer in the shop. I've always admired you for doing that," he added awkwardly.

He looked at the kitten now nestled in Beth's arms.

I saw her in the pet shop this morning when I was stuck in traffic. I rang them and they said they would keep her for me, if I came by two o'clock to put down a deposit. That's why I had to rush off at lunchtime. I collected her on my way home," David finished, looking almost boyish in his enthusiasm.

"I wanted to get something different this year. It's a milestone, the boys leaving home. Then I saw the kitten and remembered how you loved leopards. She looks like a little leopard, doesn't she?"

"Oh, David!" Beth exclaimed again. "Yes, she does."

"We'd better hurry," David then said predictably. "We'll be late at Woodlands otherwise."

"We can't go out and leave this tiny mite alone, her first night in her new home," Beth protested. "I'll ring and cancel. They'll understand."

She stroked the kitten. "I'm going to call her Velvet. Her fur is so gorgeous. And David, let's order a Chinese and a bottle of wine. It'll be just like old times." **MW**

....

ACT OF KINDNESS

After a house fire, some years back, my friend Jenny did my washing and cooked dinner for my late husband while were living in a B&B. She was such a comfort

On Patrol

Some jobs can take over your life – and Mavis is certainly as devoted as ever to the cause

By Valerie Bowes

The van had been parked there all night. It hadn't been there at nine o'clock yesterday evening, so it must have arrived some time between then and eleven pm.

Mavis Reilly checked again, taking care not to disturb the curtain by more than a millimetre. She shone her torch briefly and squinted at the neat, precise writing in her notebook. LN05 VXH. Yes, it was definitely the same vehicle.

She permitted herself a small, sour smile. It was still not fully light, the van was more than twenty-five yards away and could undoubtedly do with a wash, but she could read the numberplate as well as ever. So who were They to say she was too old for this?

It was a pity she hadn't clocked the driver, but she was pretty sure who it was. Tommy Pritchard. You didn't spend a

are. Oh-six-thirty-two." She pencilled in the time of departure. "OK."

She shifted from foot to foot. The morning was on the chilly side and she could do with a cup of tea and the loo, not necessarily in that order, but her expanding bladder would have to wait. It should be used to that.

Pride in her work, Reggie called it, when they were first married. Dedicated. Focused. After a few years, it had become *fixated, obsessional, bloody-minded*.

She shouldn't blame him. It was hard on a husband, this business. Perhaps if they'd been able to have kids, things would have been easier. But then, she'd have had to give up the job and she wasn't sure she could. Yes, she knew Reggie wanted a family, but she could never make him realise how vital her Department was, or how much she contributed to the smooth running of the country.

"What am I supposed to say, when

She shouldn't blame Reggie. It was hard on a husband, this business

lifetime in this business without getting to know the villains.

She drew back into the shadows as someone walked across the car park, but it was a blue Toyota in the far corner that blinked a greeting.

"Stock-broker type, dark hair, grey overcoat. I know I've got you." Mavis ran her finger down the list of numbers until she found the Toyota. "Right. There you

people ask me what you do?" he'd say. "OK, a job's a job, but you enjoy it too much. It's not healthy. I can't stand it much longer, Mavis."

The rows had followed; the blistering words that had made her hate him as much as he hated her. It had been almost a relief to open the front door one night and feel the emptiness emerging to greet her.

She knew he'd gone, even before ➤

she read the note, but there was no denying it was bad timing. She could have done with some help that evening. Some TLC. Someone to whom she could spill out the trials and frustrations of the day, at least.

Things had got a bit rough during her shift. Her ribs were bruised and her cheekbone stung where it had been cut. A hot bath and a hot meal were what she most wanted, but the immersion heater must have been switched off for hours. The water was stone-cold and there was nothing much in the fridge. She hadn't had time to do any shopping and she certainly didn't feel like cooking. She'd ended up phoning for a takeaway.

It was the start of a trend.

Her eyes gleamed and narrowed as a light sprang in a window of one of the little houses beyond the van. Mavis shone her torch to briefly check her information, shielding the beam from any observer in the lit window. Tommy would have to be away by oh-eight-hundred, but he was cutting it fine, as usual. It was seven-sixteen now.

whose colleagues had boasted that she could hide behind a garden cane. She'd wait. It was what she was good at.

Timing was all-important. She'd always drummed that into the new recruits.

"Steady," she'd cautioned them, when they would have rushed in and spoiled everything. "Show yourself too soon, and they'll get away. It's got to be spot-on."

She'd learned that lesson herself in the early days, and she'd never made that mistake again. The patience of a spider and constant vigilance had been her stock-in-trade. And she'd been more than good, hadn't she? She'd been the very best.

The minutes dragged by. Her eyes were on the van, but part of her brain was constantly analysing and cataloguing the noises which filtered through from outside the darkened room, judging to a nicety the time she had left before she must make her move.

She stared at the window opposite, then at her watch. Time to go.

She patted her pocket. The familiar bulge under her fingers brought the adrenaline coursing through her system. It was a good job she'd kept it when

Tommy wasn't even hurrying. Why did they think they could get away with it?

The Toyota had gone but a silver Avensis and a little red Clio came in one after the other. Mavis noted their details and saw with satisfaction that they parked on the opposite side to the white van.

No other spaces were taken. That would soon change with the morning rush, and her line of vision might be compromised. Perhaps she should seize the moment and slip down to be nearer to her quarry?

Her eyes flickered over the available cover. No. It was too risky, even for her,

They'd told her to hand in her badge.

The light in the upstairs window went off abruptly. The car park seemed darker, more shadowy. All the better, Mavis thought, slipping swiftly, like a shadow herself, to the place she'd picked out as her cover. She wouldn't be seen until it was too late, especially not by an unobservant waste of space like Tommy Pritchard.

The van was cold to her fingers as she crept around the back, keeping its protection between herself and Tommy's back door. She shivered, but not even she could have said whether it was due to the chilly morning or nerves. Every couple of seconds, she cocked her wrist to monitor the ticking figures. The door opened; she could hear Tommy calling goodbye.

Not yet! Not yet! She crouched, ready to pounce, willing the numbers on her watch to hurry. The magic oh-eight-hundred clicked into place.

Mavis straightened and let her pent

breath trickle through her lips. She sauntered nonchalantly around the van.

Tommy was walking towards her. Not even hurrying. Why did they think they could get away with it? He stopped in his tracks, ran his hand over his shaven head.

"Aw, fer. . . not again! Just leave it out, willya?"

Her fingertips lightly brushed the grimy white paintwork. Gimlet eyes fixed themselves on the numberplate. Mavis Reilly was in her element.

"Is this your vehicle, sir?"

"You know it is!" Tommy took a visible hold of his temper. "I've told you before, Mizz Reilly, it's legit."

"Not after eight o'clock, son."

Mavis smiled in grim triumph and reached for her pocket, but the voice behind her made her spin round.

"What's going on here?"

There he was, the little Hitler. This

was her patch. Why didn't he just let her get on with it?

"Come on, Mavis," Brian Bramber said. "You know you shouldn't be doing this."

"If you did your job, I wouldn't have to," she snapped.

He shook his head wearily, but the lightning snatch he made for the thing in her hand took her by surprise. *Reflexes must be slowing. Must practise more.*

He waved it reproachfully. "And you shouldn't still have this. Should have turned it in with the rest a month ago."

"I can run rings round you, Bramber. You're not a patch on me," she hissed.

"Doesn't alter facts, Mavis. You can't use this, you're retired. It's official. As of last month." He tucked the pad of Fixed Penalty Notices away in the breast pocket of his uniform.

"*Parking is free to residents from eighteen hundred hours to oh-eight-hundred,*" she intoned, quoting the huge Pay and Display board by the car park entrance. She consulted her watch with a flourish. "It is now oh-eight-oh-three and thirty seconds. Book him, Bramber."

"Here! That's not fair!" Tommy said. "I'd have been gone if it weren't for her!"

Bramber sighed.

"It's all right, sir. No ticket. But what are we going to do with you, Mavis? Once a traffic warden, always a traffic warden."

ACT OF KINDNESS

I broke my shoulder and couldn't drive. A friend took me to stay with my cousin in Somerset, a round trip of about 400 miles – and picked me up again when my visit was over.

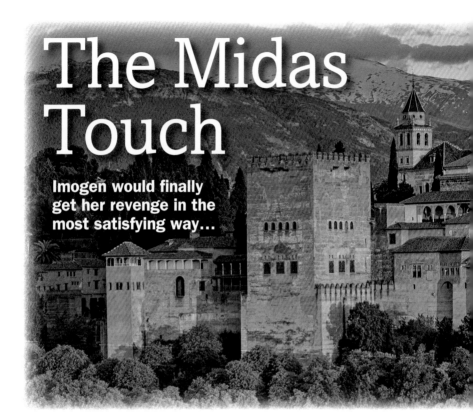

The Midas Touch

Imogen would finally get her revenge in the most satisfying way…

By DB Court

"Paella y una copa de vino blanco." Imogen Hardacre relaxed her shoulders and smiled. Asking for paella and a glass of wine was easy enough. But after two days in Spain her Spanish didn't flow the way it had done when she'd first left University. Not surprising. Back then she'd lived and breathed the Spanish language that had gained her a First degree. It had been her way to escape, to begin a new life.

"Copa grande o pequeña, senorita?"

Big or small? Good question. Even if she didn't feel it, she may as well do her best to look the part of a woman on holiday, enjoying herself. "Grande, por favor."

It was hard to believe ten years had raced by since she'd last been sitting in this same outdoor restaurant, high up on the hillside of the Albaicín. It was a quirky place, little more than a thin strip of land hanging in the air. Only eight tables, a canopied bar and a tiny wooden building with marble floors for a toilet.

She peered over the outer wall to her right at a sheer drop onto rough rocky land, wild with cacti, arid gardens and several cats. As well as giving her a good view of all the comings and goings through the restaurant's one gated entrance, from this table she could gaze far across the valley of Granada, with its narrow streets and medieval cathedral, and be blessed with the most stunning view of the Alhambra Palace, crafted by Moorish kings. In the evening sunshine the palace slowly turned the

colour of the red earth, used to make those immense outer walls, that gave it its name.

The waiter deftly placed down her glass. She took a sip of wine, cold and dry, and fragrant with lemons and melon and sunshine. Or was that simply Granada stirring her imagination?

No one paid any attention to her, dining alone. She'd learnt the knack of making herself invisible. Besides, being alone was the choice she'd made when she'd brought her three-year relationship with Peter to an end four months ago. The relationship was sapping the life out of both of them. She finally had to admit that her heart wasn't in it. How could it be? Long ago someone else had broken her heart so badly that she'd never allowed herself to love again.

She took another sip of wine, a sweeter taste than self-pity.

Long ago someone had broken her heart so badly she could never love again

It was time to re-awaken her forgotten knowledge while waiting for paella. She pulled the Spanish newspaper from her bag and did a slow read of the front page, the spanish vocabulary beginning to feel as familiar as a long lost friend.

There was only one story worthy of the front page, all about the greatest ➤

jewellery thief – la mayor ladrona de joyas – of the 21st century. There was no need to translate the name everyone had given this thief: Midas, the king with the knack of turning everything to gold at the touch of a finger. This modern Midas was not quite a master alchemist, but a thief able to steal priceless possessions, always jewellery, and then vanish away. There'd been six sizeable thefts so far in less than two years. In the last one a necklace worth over £400,000 had been stolen from a house in Kensington, London. Even in the black and white photo the necklace looked incredible. Art Deco, with a huge stone at its centre surrounded by so many tiny diamonds, they must surely set the world alight. Imogen suspected passion must be involved, a passion bordering on madness, followed by cruel betrayal. Otherwise how could the theft of a prized possession be so easy?

"Muchas gracias." She lay down her newspaper, her raised fork diving into the plate of paella before the waiter had time to invite her to enjoy her meal.

He laughed, said the words anyway. "Disfruta de su comida, señorita!"

The paella tasted delicious, and she would certainly enjoy every bite. Coming to Spain had been the right thing for her to do for so many reasons. Already she felt refreshed, sensing that this was a time for new beginnings.

She glanced up. Five new customers had arrived, making a grand entrance, laughing loudly and talking in English, filling the restaurant with their arrival as if they owned the place. One man, surrounded by four women, all perfectly manicured, all blonde. A bit of a cliché, especially the way they danced around him like puppets on a string, even allowing him to seat them.

"I must have the best view of each one of you," he declared loudly, for all to hear.

The man glanced Imogen's way. He looked straight through her. But she knew it was him, recognised him immediately and her heart gave a thump in her chest. It felt as if she'd been waiting for this moment forever, to face the man who had been like a plague eating away at her for ten long years, ruining every attempt she'd made to find happiness. He'd ripped out her heart, torn it into little pieces, but this was her chance to break free of this obsession and get on with her life.

She sipped her wine, studied the faces of the two women she could see, both of them perfectly made-up, painted mouths laughing, eyes all eyeshadow and mascara. Their hands fluttered as they spoke, sending a hint of their heady perfume towards her.

It had always been this way from the moment she'd first set eyes on Simon Miller. From the day he'd joined sixth form, with his dark hair a little too long for the teacher's tastes, his tie always loose, top button undone as if he was about to undress. Girls had flocked to him, surrounded his every step, followed him wherever he led as if he was a Pied Piper playing the only tune they wanted to hear. Women loved his sense of humour, the way he made life seem exciting, the way he seemed to be interested in each and every one of them. His reckless attitude to love only seemed to add to his already powerful magnetism, creating a terrible illusion that could make a woman believe, one day, she would be the chosen one.

She had loved the way he would run his hands through her long red hair and stroke her skin, the way he would dwell on her every word, laugh and kiss the tip of her nose. Full of raging hormones, her sixteen-year-old self had made the same mistake as all of the others, toppled head first into his trap only to find that she was unable

And now he was here, in Granada, her favourite place on earth. She ate more slowly, took her time. She could look at him all she liked because, so far, he had no idea she was there.

The taller woman sitting to his right was stunning, her long blonde hair curling around her shoulders, the black dress tailored to show off her figure to perfection. Her long slender fingers touched the necklace she wore, an emerald stone set on onyx, with over a hundred tiny diamonds sparkling against the dark background, and yet more diamonds woven into the fine chain that shimmered against the woman's neck. She leant towards Simon with such a look of gratitude on her face there could be no doubt that the necklace had been a gift from him. Perhaps she was his favourite.

Imogen folded her newspaper, slid it

The jewellery thief was so successful that he had gained a nickname: Midas

to ever truly escape. She'd thought she was different, that he would love her back. Unlike the others she was academically just as clever as him – cleverer as it turned out. For a while he'd risen to the challenge, thriving on every new contest to try and match her achievements. But in the end he'd given up competing against her. So she'd won her place at Cambridge, and he'd settled for some red brick university studying Social Sciences. As if he needed to learn any more about the psychology of manipulating people.

He had said he loved her. Over and over, he'd said those words, even declared his love for her to others. *I'll shout it from the rooftops if that will make you believe me*, he'd told her. Lies, such powerful lies they'd mangled her heart, leaving a toxic residue of unfinished business that had festered into an obsession.

back into her bag then shrugged off the dull grey jacket that helped to make her invisible, revealing the emerald velvet dress beneath, worn like a second skin, sleeveless, low cut. Slowly she undid the grips that held her neat bun in place then shook her head a little to set her long red hair free. With a tilt of her chin, she turned to gaze at the Alhambra, now bathed in the flame of sunset, and knew that same light would be touching her hair, adding to its natural fire.

Next thing she knew he was there, Simon Miller, like a moth to a flame. He laughed, placed his palms on her table and leant in. "It's you, isn't it? Your stunning red hair, the tilt of your nose. Why, I'd recognise you anywhere. Imogen Hardacre! I can't believe it's you. Still as beautiful as ever."

"Hello Simon."

Close up, she saw that too much drinking had added lines to his face. His teeth ➔

had yellowed. His tie hugged his throat, neatly knotted, with not a single shirt button undone. No hint of the skin beneath now. His once rich black hair had greyed a little and thinned.

"May I sit with you?"

"Won't your…" She thought to say entourage, but didn't want to sound bitter, "…won't your friends miss you?"

"The wine's flowing freely. They'll be fine. It's so wonderful to see you. What are you doing in Spain, and why are you sitting all alone? Oh, I remember now, you studied Spanish at Uni, didn't you? So, let me guess, you're teaching or a tour guide, living in Granada, something like that?" He sat down, leaned in further.

"Not even close!" she said.

"It's been, what? – ten years since you dumped me… so fill me in."

knocked over. "No, I'm working," she said, allowing her voice to sound casual as she reached into her bag as if searching for her purse. She had to rummage a little before her fingers slid around what she was after, wrapped around it, felt it secure in her hand, made ready. She looked up, smiled, waited.

"So if you're not a teacher or a translator or a tour guide, what are you?" His never-ending curiosity had always been Simon's downfall.

With a practiced hand she clamped the handcuffs around his wrist, swift, precise, ensuring there would be no chance of escape. "I'm Detective Chief Inspector Imogen Hardacre, and I'm arresting you, Simon Miller, on suspicion of theft …"

"Is this a joke?"

"You do not have to say anything. But it may harm your defence if you do not

Everything had gone even better than she could ever have hoped for

He managed to conjure up the same expression he'd manufactured ten years ago, his attempt at appearing heart-broken.

"I had cause to dump you, Simon. You kept forgetting who your girlfriend was."

"Yes, well, I never thought…"

"You never thought I would find out." Imogen laughed, laughed a little more when she saw the red flush creeping up from his neck and covering his face. Not shame. That was not the cause. Definitely not. More likely anger. Simon had never liked dealing with women who didn't fall at his feet. They'd been discarded swiftly, if he'd bothered with them at all.

But it didn't fit with his image to stand up and march away in a huff. "So, you're on holiday," he said, his spine more rigid, his voice now curt, less interested in the answer.

With her dinner over Imogen drained her glass, moved it aside so it wouldn't get

mention, when questioned, something which you later rely on in court. Anything you do say may be given in evidence. And, no. It's not a joke. You've grown careless Simon, letting your women-friends wear the profits of your latest heist. What were you thinking?"

"This was a trap, wasn't it? You, your face, your hair! You were deliberately chosen, weren't you, to ensnare me!"

He was right, but it was best to concentrate on police procedures and not respond. Satisfying though, that she had been the bait, and he had taken a big bite without hesitation.

Simon actually growled at her then, a roar of frustration as his eyes darted every which way, desperately searching for an escape route. He glanced over the wall, assessing the drop and whether he was strong enough to drag her with him, tied as he was to her, by the handcuffs.

"I wouldn't if I were you," she said. "It's a hell of a drop. Even if you manage to land without snapping your leg in two, you'd have to drag me along behind you, which might slow your escape considerably. Plus, there are police down there waiting. In fact, look around you. Tonight, all the other customers in this lovely little restaurant are my officers. See, already two of them are doing a very efficient job of rounding up your lady friends, especially the one flaunting the necklace you stole from Kensington last week. Are you careless, Simon, or are you just reckless? I can't quite make up my mind."

"How did you know where to find me?"

"It's your misfortune that these days the police from different countries talk to each other, help each other nail the criminals. You were seen two days ago in Granada sitting at a café in the plaza outside of the cathedral. Or, more to the point, someone noticed the lady you were sitting with was wearing a necklace that was a dead-ringer for a diamond choker stolen in France a months ago."

He licked his dry lips. She could almost feel sorry for him. Almost.

"Tell me, how did you steal the jewellery so easily?"

"Women fall for me, tell me their secrets. They make it easy."

"Why flaunt what you've stolen?"

He smiled, but beads of perspiration peppered his face. "Well, naturally, I did it so that I would have the pleasure of seeing you again, Imogen, my red-haired beauty, the love of my life."

"No, Simon. You did it because you haven't changed. You always think you'll get away with it."

As she left the restaurant Imogen thanked the staff for agreeing to aid the police and playing their part so well. The

Spanish language now rolled off her tongue. The ability she was afraid she'd lost had been reawakened.

"Todo salió como había planeado?" the manager said.

Had everything gone as she'd planned? Imogen smiled. In fact, everything had gone even better than she could have hoped for. She placed her free hand on her heart and said, "Si! Mejor gracias. He sido liberada de mis cadenas."

The manager, not surprisingly looked puzzled at her reply. Luckily Simon Miller, still handcuffed to her wrist, had never bothered to learn a single word in any language but his own, so he didn't have a clue what she'd said. She was glad he would never know how he'd held her heart trapped in his hands all these years. She felt even happier, though, that Simon would be locked up in a prison cell, while she, at last, had been set free. Ⓜ

• •

ACT OF KINDNESS

Researching WW1 while writing a children's book, I discovered that over 500,000 cats helped the men on the front line endure that terrible war. Animals: our generous-hearted friends.

The Mistress And The Maid

It had been so long, but would their swapping places reveal what was truly in the Major's heart?

By Kate Finnemore

I am far from certain, Miss Charlotte," I said, choosing my words with care, "that we should be doing this. It is deception."

"Deception – phooey! Look, all we are doing is swapping places. I will be the maid and you shall be the lady. For a few hours, that is all. Where is the harm in that?"

"For the few hours Major Blakeney happens to be visiting." Wearing just my pantaloons and corset now, I slipped my dress over Miss Charlotte's head and shoulders, and tightened the lacings at the back.

"Don't be impertinent, Robinson." She shifted from one side to the other,

I picked up Miss Charlotte's dress – the dress I was to wear – from the armchair, but instead of putting it on I simply stood, cautious as always, holding it to my chest. "What do you think your parents would say if they knew what we were doing?"

She tore her gaze away from the mirror. "Mamma and papa? They wouldn't stop me. They refuse me nothing."

More's the pity, I thought. It had been a busy morning. A messenger had arrived from the Prince Regent inviting Miss Charlotte's mother and father for a spot of sea-bathing further along the coast at Brighton. They, of course, had accepted the invitation with alacrity.

Shortly after their departure, however, another messenger had arrived, this time

"I will be the maid and you shall be the lady, for a few hours, that is all"

examining her image in the large framed mirror that stood on the dressing table. A smile played over her features. "Tie the apron, will you. And place the cap. Hmm, I look good, even in this, don't I?"

I smiled, recognising her need for reassurance. "You do, Miss Charlotte."

"You must call me Robinson. And I shall call you Miss Charlotte."

from Major Blakeney. The Major was at long last home from the wars in France, the messenger said, and couldn't wait to pay his respects to his dearest cousin and fiancée. Since business called him to London the next day, he looked forward to visiting her that afternoon.

The colour had swept from Miss Charlotte's face. She'd swayed, and I'd ➤

put my arms out ready to catch her. But when she straightened her spine and told the messenger to convey her gracious thanks to Major Blakeney, I couldn't help admiring her courage.

She'd waited until we were alone before saying, "I have an idea."

I'd been unhappy when she first outlined her scheme. Now I'd had time to think it over, I was even more unhappy. "Major Blakeney is going to know as soon as he sees me that I am not you."

"I don't think so. I haven't seen him for four years. I have changed a lot in that time. Besides, you and I are the same age, we have the same dark hair – yours is almost as fine and lustrous as mine – and being my maid, you have acquired

If it helped her gauge the man she was to marry, I would agree to it

some of the manners and bearing of a lady."

Remembering my place, I said nothing, burying my nose instead in the dress I held to my chest, inhaling the sweet scent of roses that wafted up from the feather-light fabric.

"Robinson –" She came away from the mirror, and there was a different, somehow shaky edge to her voice. Taking the dress from me, she held it out and up, and I knew I had no choice but to put it on.

"I am scared, Robinson," she said. "The last time I saw him was the Christmas I was fifteen. He was a year older and covered in spots."

My heart sank. "Not the, um, pox?"

"No, stupid. Just the spots horrid boys get on their faces as they grow into manhood. And he *was* horrid. Always teasing me. He cut two of my ringlets off that Christmas."

I knew better than to laugh. I let the dress slip over my head and shoulders, reaching behind me to tighten the lacing.

"My future happiness – my whole life – depends on this man," she went on, and I could hear she was close to tears. "He has spent years in the army fighting the Frenchies. What if he has turned into even more of a bully? What if, when we are married, what if he is unkind to me?"

All at once my heart went out to her. Her marriage to Major Blakeney had, I'd been told, been arranged many years before as a means of uniting two branches of the family and two neighbouring estates. If she were lucky, Miss Charlotte would find happiness with the man her parents had chosen for her. But there were no guarantees, unfortunately.

I on the other hand had no worries on that score. An orphan, and the penniless ward of the vicar and his wife, I'd received an education that made work as a lady's maid possible, but marriage was less likely. The best I could hope for was a life of service.

There was a lump in my throat as I took Miss Charlotte's hands in mine. "Don't worry, Miss Charlotte – Robinson," I corrected myself with heavy emphasis. "If it helps you gauge the man he has turned into before you have to commit yourself irrevocably, then yes, I shall play at being you for a few hours."

"I knew you would understand." Her eyes glittered and I had to blink rapidly to hold my own tears back.

A sound reached me from outside. We looked at each other.

"Horses. He is here."

Together we ran from Miss Charlotte's

staircase to the ground floor, we'd almost reached the bottom as Croshaw and a footman crossed the hall. The butler's frowning glance darted from Miss Charlotte, dressed in my habitual uniform of pale blue dress, white apron and cap, to myself, decked out in all the finery of a lady.

"Give us a few seconds, Croshaw," Miss Charlotte said, and we ran on across the hall.

The drawing room windows were open, letting in a warm, early summer breeze heavy with the scents of roses and honeysuckle. My heart was beating fast as I perched straight-backed on one of a pair of chairs in the centre of the room.

"Over there," I whispered, pointing, and Miss Charlotte picked up her embroidery and went to sit in one corner of the room. It was a good vantage point: she'd be able to observe Major Blakeney without drawing attention to herself. For him, she'd simply be a maid, to be ignored.

A tap at the door. I rose to my feet, clasping my gloved hands in front of me.

"Major Blakeney, Miss Charlotte." Croshaw was directing his words to a point midway between his mistress and myself, and I felt my mouth curving into a smile.

The Major, tall and broad-shouldered, strode towards me on long, shapely legs. He'd removed his hat, holding it in the crook of his arm, revealing thick dark hair that flopped down over his forehead and curled over his collar. My breath caught. He really was most presentable.

"Miss Charlotte." He stopped before me, bringing his heels together with a →

dressing room to her bedroom. Standing back from the window in case he should see us, I was just in time to catch fleeting impressions before Major Blakeney drew too close to the house to be seen any more: a clean-shaven, regular face, the relaxed but straight-backed posture of a man at ease with horses, a dazzling bright red uniform coat. His man, dressed in sober dark blues and greys, rode at a respectful distance behind him.

"He certainly looks presentable," I said.

"He does," she agreed.

"Come on, we must get to the drawing room before Croshaw lets him and his man in."

Running down the wide marble

snap and bowing his head. His man, close behind, greeted me in the same military fashion.

"Major Blakeney." I dipped into a curtsey. "Pray take a seat."

Croshaw cleared his throat. "Will there be anything else, Miss Charlotte?" Again, he addressed a midway point.

"Yes," I replied. "Ask Atkins to bring tea for the two of us."

"Very well, Miss."

The Major and I both sat. I was nervous. I had to make conversation with this man for goodness knew how long. What if he found me out for the impostor I was? I looked away from him, towards Miss Charlotte. She made an impatient "get on with it" gesture with her hand, and I turned back to the Major, swallowing to ease the dryness in my mouth. "Did you have a good journey over here this afternoon?"

"Yes indeed. Riding across the Downs on a beautiful day like today – what could be better?" he asked, glancing across at his man who stood on one side of the fireplace.

As he went on to give me further details of the journey, Atkins the housekeeper came in, together with a maid carrying a tray of tea things. Soon there was a cup of fragrant tea for each of us, while a candied fruit scone, still warm from the oven, balanced on the edge of each saucer.

"And how are General and Lady Blakeney? Keeping well, I hope?"

Fortunately, the two families were

close and, accompanying Miss Charlotte, I had visited most of the Blakeneys in our neighbourhood and therefore knew who to enquire after. I think I only made one mistake, calling a great-aunt of his Hannah instead of Harriet. But the Major – clearly a true gentleman – didn't correct me.

I was still on edge, fearful of being found out. Yet at the same time, I was rather enjoying myself.

The Major was good to look at – the spots that had afflicted him at the age of sixteen had vanished, leaving no trace. He had all his teeth, the front ones at least. He was softly-spoken, with none of

a

the superior drawl I associated with the aristocratic families in the area, including his own. His years in France must have had their effect.

He didn't slurp his tea or drop scone crumbs down his front. And what he had to say – once we'd got past enquiries after his family and Miss Charlotte's – was extremely interesting.

At times, though, I noticed a carefulness about him, a sense that he was watching his words, that made me somewhat wary. Was there something going on? Or was it some problem with his man? I wondered, intercepting yet another glance he sent his valet.

I looked across at Miss Charlotte who still sat in the corner, embroidery on her lap, her gaze intent on the Major. I hoped she was forming the same good impression of the man that I was, and that she'd be reassured by it.

"…it was only noon, but the men were exhausted…"

The Major was giving me a fascinating account of his part in the battle at Waterloo. I looked towards his man, thinking he too must have lived through the horror of it all – and for an instant I

"But I shall not bore you any longer, Miss –"

"Oh but I wasn't at all bored." I beamed him a smile. "Though, perhaps, as it is such a beautiful afternoon, we could go for a walk in the gardens?"

For the sheer wicked joy of it, I went on, "Robinson, fetch me my bonnet and shawl, the one with the paisley border."

I couldn't help it. My smile broadened as I watched her get up and cross the room. For once I could order Miss Charlotte about – and she had no choice but to obey.

The look she sent me just before she closed the door behind her would have made Hell itself freeze over.

I believe you are not who you claim to be, sir."

"Ah."

No bluster, no denial, I noted. I'd waited until the four of us were outside. Hands clasped behind his back, the man I knew was not Major Blakeney walked at my side along a gravel path that wound gently downhill to the lake.

Miss Charlotte, looking somewhat put out to be carrying a small basket of

Suddenly I understood why the Major kept looking across at his valet

simply stared, barely registering what I was seeing.

The valet was gesturing with his hand, not a "get on with it" gesture like the one Miss Charlotte had sent me, but a signal to "finish – now".

Suddenly I understood why the Major kept looking at his valet, why he hadn't corrected my mistake over his great-aunt's name. I felt laughter bubbling up inside me, laughter it was an effort to suppress.

refreshment, followed some twenty yards behind us, while the man I knew was not a valet strode along a few paces behind her, carrying two folding chairs and a table. The two of them walked in silence. My mistress, of course, would never dream of conversing with a man she considered to be a servant.

"In fact," I went on, and could hardly keep the laughter from my voice, "I believe you and Major Blakeney have done precisely what Miss Charlotte and ➜

I have done."

"Miss Charlotte and –" He stopped abruptly, turning to look at me, then, "Well, I'll be –" He shook his head, mouth widening into a broad grin, and glanced behind him. "So that's Miss Charlotte." He turned back to me. "And you are?"

"Her maid. Robinson. Mary Robinson."

"George Fraser. At your service, Miss," he replied.

"My mistress hadn't seen Major Blakeney for so long, you see," I said as we continued to walk along, "that she keeps in a silk pouch on a cord round his neck. Close to his heart."

"Ah." My relief was immense.

As one, it seemed, we stopped, turning to look at the two figures who kept a respectful twenty yards behind us. They were now walking side by side. I had the impression they had exchanged a few words.

Mr Fraser's eyes, alight with mischief, met mine. "I am rather enjoying being the master. I am disinclined to reveal what we have discovered straight away."

I laughed. "I agree. I too am rather

"I am disinclined to reveal what we have discovered straight away"

didn't know what to expect."

"My master told me this morning he would rather be fighting a whole company of Frenchies than making the re-acquaintance of Miss Charlotte."

My mouth went dry. "Because he doesn't like her?"

"Because he likes her too much. But he is a proud man and didn't want to make a fool of himself. We changed roles so he could see if his feelings for her had remained the same – and if she might feel something for him."

"Tell me," I said, "is the Major a bully? A cruel man?"

"Not in the least."

"And he has feelings, deep feelings, for Miss Charlotte?"

"He has two ringlets of her hair that he

enjoying being the mistress."

As I looked into his eyes, my heart missed a beat. We were so alike, I sensed, in so many ways. And if, as seemed probable, the Major and my mistress were to be married, then George Fraser and I would have ample opportunity to get to know each other better. I was looking forward to it. Very much so. **MW**

● ●

DON'T MISS IT

For features, fiction, cookery, travel, puzzles, health news, and your favourite celebrities, My Weekly is on sale every Tuesday

✦ 2011 saw the movie *Sanctum*, a cave diving thriller loosely based on a real life experience – it is tense and claustrophobic!

✦ In 2016 Blake Lively played a surfer who goes head to head with a great white shark in the nerve-shredding *The Shallows*.

✦ *20 Thousand Leagues Under The Sea* was first released in 1954, an adaptation of Jules Verne's classic novel. For its time, it was a massive technical achievement

FANCY THAT!

Fascinating facts on **Underwater Movies!**

✦ 1975's adaptation of Peter Benchley's *Jaws* gave us a now classic soundtrack and a few oft-quoted great lines, like, "We're gonna need a bigger boat!"

✦ *Deepstar Six* (1989) was a typically '80s over-the-top movie with an underwater nuclear base and a creature from the deep that threatens all of mankind!

✦ The Pixar animation *Finding Nemo* (2003) follows a father's quest to rescue his son from a dentist's aquarium... perfect family entertainment.

✦ In 1977, *The Deep* was another Peter Benchley adaptation, in which a bikini-clad Jacqueline Bisset make diving cool and sexy!

Creature from the Black Lagoon, released in 1954, is a horror classic in which an Amazon geology expedition is terrorised by the titular monster

✦ Last but not least 2018's *Aquaman* is an action-packed adventure in a vast undersea world... and who wouldn't want to see Jason Momoa wield a trident?

Bollywood Dreams

The man of her dreams, but who was her real hero…?

By Julia Douglas

"Manish, Manish, Manish!" Jamil's glasses flashed as he shuffled patient notes in the A&E office. "What's so great about Manish Kaif anyway?"

"He's only the most eligible bachelor in India!" Pari kissed the DVD case and slapped it to the bosom of her junior doctor's coat with a sigh.

"And he's coming to Birmingham to be in a recruitment film with Pari!" Cliona squealed as she snatched the DVD from her colleague to swoon over the film star.

"I bet they picked you because you look just like his ex, Nalina." The redheaded nurse pointed excitedly to Manish's co-star on the movie cover.

"Do you think so?" Pari craned over Cliona's shoulder to admire the exotic couple, who were clinking champagne flutes across the bonnet of a Ferrari. "Who'd have thought they'd have picked me out of the whole staff to be in advert with the biggest star in Bollywood!"

"He can't even act," Jamil scorned.

"Oh look, we're making Jamil jealous," Cliona teased.

"Don't worry, Jamil." Pari made a display of pushing back her fellow doctor's floppy fringe with her long fingers. "You know you'll always be my first love. Well, you and Manish!"

Jamil pulled away in a huff and Pari giggled. She'd known Jamil since they were children and always enjoyed teasing him. He looked cute when he was embarrassed.

"You can see why they chose Manish for the recruitment campaign, can't you?" said Cliona. "If all the patients looked like him we'd be overrun with doctors!"

I can't believe you really are a doctor." Manish smiled from the bed where he was reclining in a hospital gown like a Roman emperor in a toga. "When I saw you, I thought you must be a TV star."

"No, I'm a doctor – trust me!" Pari tried not to be mesmerised by eyes as tempting as dark chocolates.

She'd wondered if the film star would

Then I want you to take his hand and gaze reassuringly into his eyes."

"OK," she squeaked.

Behind the camera and lights, she saw Jamil watching from the doorway of the private room, until an assistant closed the door in his face to shut out distractions.

Pari had taken the blood pressure of hundreds of patients, but she'd never felt

She had known Jamil since they were children and always enjoyed teasing him

be a disappointment in real life. Jamil had reckoned he'd be short and spotty off screen. But Pari had never met a man so magnetic.

"OK, Pari," said the director. "You're going to take Manish's blood pressure while he gives his speech to the camera.

as self conscious as she did wrapping the cuff around Manish's bicep.

As she met his smouldering gaze at the end of the scene, it felt like her whole body was on fire.

"And cut!" said the director. "That was brilliant." ➡

"Thanks to the beautiful Pari!" Manish declared, still holding her hand. "You'll have to come to Mumbai and be in my next film."

"Oh, I can't act!" Pari tossed back her hair with a giggle.

"I'm serious." Manish sat up and swung his legs off the side of the bed. "You're perfect for the part."

"I can't even speak Hindi," Pari protested.

"They can overdub your voice." Manish shrugged. "But that face…" He touched her jaw like it was fine china. "You'll be a bigger box office draw than Nalina ever was. Let's discuss it over dinner, shall we?"

That evening, Pari could barely believe she was riding through the city in a cab with one of the world's biggest film stars.

"See that tower block?" Some of Manish's original Brummie accent broke through his polished international tones. "I grew up there, in the poorest part of Birmingham. Now I live in the best apartment in Mumbai. I've got a yacht in Dubai, a Lamborghini…"

He pulled a phone from his pocket and the car's interior was suddenly lit up by pictures of his sun-kissed life on the other side of the world.

"A girl with your looks could have all of that and more, Pari. It's like winning the Lottery when you go over there."

"But wouldn't I have to audition for the part?" Pari asked nervously. "I mean, isn't it up to the director, or the producer?"

Manish cut her off with a snort.

"I'm Manish Kaif." He thumbed his chest. "The biggest box office draw in India. If I want you in my movie, they'll have you in the movie, or they don't get me in the movie."

I feel like Cinderella," Pari exclaimed to Cliona in the A&E office the next day.

"You're not actually going?" Jamil clanged a bedpan onto the desk in astonishment.

"Of course I'm going." Pari couldn't help being rattled by the strength of her oldest friend's response. "Who else gets an opportunity like this?"

"But he's a notorious playboy," Jamil blurted. "Everyone knows what he's like."

"I'm only going to make a film," Pari snapped. "I'm not going to marry him."

Her cheeks burned as she relived the lingering kiss Manish had bestowed on her when he dropped her off at her parents'

the mud, he even resented her coming.

Well, it was his loss. Manish had opened her eyes to a world of possibilities that she'd never even considered. After being a swot all through high school and medical school, she reckoned it was time that she started to live a little.

Feeling liberated in the swishy low-cut dress and expensive perfume that Manish had given her, she wove her way through the scented pot plants to their table.

The actor had his back to her and a phone to his ear.

"That's right, a doctor!" he hissed. "Brains as well as beauty!"

As she passed his shoulder, he

Her cheeks burned as she relived the lingering kiss Manish bestowed on her

house at midnight. It felt too soon to tell her friends about that, though.

"I thought you'd be pleased for me," she said, hurt.

"I am, but…"

"Oh, just ignore him, Pari!" Cliona cut in. "You're going to be a star – and you deserve it!"

A s Pari returned from the powder room, she gazed in awe at the view from the 34th floor rooftop restaurant. The darkening sky was a magical shade of purple and the moon hung like a golden ball above its shimmering reflection in the lilac ocean.

The lights of Mumbai enclosed the bay like a grotto. It certainly beat any view of rainy Birmingham.

She wished Jamil was there to share the moment. He'd been such a constant in her life that it felt strange to be so far away without him. But then, the bookish doctor would never have taken her on such an adventure. He was such a stick in

muttered, "Gotta go now, mate."

"Who were you talking to?" Pari demanded as she sat opposite him.

"Just a friend." He pocketed the phone.

"Did you only bring me here so you could brag about it?" she asked, stung.

"Of course not." He gave her a wounded look that would have melted a cinema screen. "But look at you, Pari. When a man meets such an angel, can't he be forgiven for wanting to brag?"

T he doorman bowed as they left the restaurant. Manish's scarlet Lamborghini slid to a halt in front of them and a car hop stepped out, leaving the meaty engine running.

Heady from the champagne and rich food, Pari reckoned she could get used to such service.

She was about to step into the sleek sports car when a flashbulb startled her.

"The paparazzi get everywhere," Manish grumbled. "I don't know how they knew I was here." ➜

As Manish gunned the throaty engine and squealed the tyres, Pari glanced over her shoulder to where the photographer was still snapping pictures.

She remembered Manish's furtive phone call earlier. Had he tipped off the press himself?

She forgot the thought when Manish said, "Are you coming back to my penthouse for a nightcap?"

So where's the King of Bollywood?" sneered a male dancer in a golden turban, leather waistcoat and britches.

"Probably still busy getting his legs waxed," sniggered a woman dressed as a harem girl.

Two dozen bejewelled performers were kicking their heels on a soundstage that was dripping with more gilt than Aladdin's cave.

The cameramen, lighting technicians

Now, though, Pari realised that she hadn't seen the assistant for a while. Had she been absent as long as Manish?

Pari cursed the state of constant suspicion that her new boyfriend roused in her. She wanted to trust him, but how she wished he was more like Jamil – a man who didn't need constant female attention to validate himself.

It was pointless comparing the amorous Manish to the stoic Jamil, however. Her lifelong pal was just that, and he had never even flirted with her.

If he had, she wouldn't even be in India, would she?

At that moment, Manish returned to the set, his chest puffed out like a peacock in a purple silk shirt and blindingly white britches.

"So what are we all just standing around for?" he demanded of all the faces that had turned his way. "Let's get this

Sometimes it seemed the whole world revolved around Manish's every whim

and everyone else in the crew were getting equally restive.

"I'll go to his trailer and see what he's up to," Pari offered, embarrassed by the delay.

"No, Pari." Krish, the fatherly, grey-haired director stepped forward to block her. "Don't you go."

"Why not?" Pari searched his imploring eyes and wondered what she saw. Was it pity, as if he knew something she didn't?

Her mind flashed back to earlier, when she'd noticed Manish chatting to a pretty makeup assistant. She'd felt a stab of jealousy but had said nothing.

Every girl who met Manish swooned over him and he treated them all like they were special. It wasn't flirting, he insisted, just a duty to keep his fans happy.

dance number in the can, shall we?"

As Manish strode to his position, no one questioned the man they all depended on for a living. But as Pari glanced in the direction he'd come from, she saw that the makeup assistant had reappeared.

Coincidence, she told herself. For how could she prove otherwise?

The flashbulbs went off like a firework display as Pari extended her leg from the limousine. Climbing from a car in a silver dress split to the hip was a perilous manoeuvre in itself without having to perform it while dazzled.

Fortunately, Manish was gallantly waiting in a tuxedo to help her up and onto the red carpet.

He placed an ostentatious kiss on her

hand, then slipped his arm around her waist as they posed for more pictures.

The Filmfare Awards were Bollywood's Oscars, televised across India.

The film they'd just wrapped wouldn't be out for months but Manish was up for his third "Black Lady" as Best Actor for one of his previous features. Pictures of him and Pari, meanwhile, had been lighting up the gossip websites for weeks.

As they walked past the snappers and reporters surging against the red velvet rope, questions came thick and fast.

"Is it true you're getting engaged?" someone called.

Pari would have liked to know that herself.

"You'll have to wait and see," Manish winked at the reporter as he swept her along.

Sometimes it seemed to Pari that the whole world revolved around Manish's every whim, and she was as helplessly caught in his dizzying orbit as every other moth.

Dressed like a fairytale princess on his arm, she'd never felt so far from her rounds on the wards with Jamil and Cliona. At least there she felt like her feet were touching the ground.

Inside the futuristic Bandra Kurla Complex, the VIP hospitality suite was bubbling like a pressure cooker. While Manish disappeared into a crowd of back-slapping celebrities, Pari suddenly felt lost and alone among the heartily chatting actors and directors.

Needing to anchor herself, she squeezed through the throng in search of her escort. Her heart leapt with relief when she saw him in the corner with his back to her. She was just about to go to him when she realised he was with Nalina Chander, his famous ex-girlfriend. He was almost squeezing the slinky actress against the wall.

Creeping closer, unseen, she heard Manish snort.

"You must be joking if you think I'm interested in Pari. She can't act, she can't dance. She almost ruined the film!"

Nalina stroked his jaw with a fingertip and gave him a feline smile. Then, as quick as a cat, her face twisted in fury.

"And if you think you could win me back simply by making me jealous, then *you* must be the one who's joking!" She slapped his face with the sharp sound of a whip crack.

Everyone in the room turned to stare, except Pari, who'd already seen enough.

Feeling like she'd been slapped herself, she turned and shoved her way through the well-tailored crowd. Blinded by tears, she blundered through a door marked Emergency Exit and stumbled into a cool alley, gasping for breath.

She was dressed for one of the most glittering events in the world but there was no way she could sit through the ceremony with Manish, knowing all his lies. How had she ever let herself be seduced by his empty glamour?

Wanting only to get on the first ➜

flight home, she walked blindly until she realised she was nearing the front of the complex.

Ahead of her was a huge crowd of film fans hoping for a glimpse of the stars.

She looked around for a different escape route, then saw a smaller commotion within the throng. A man in a tux was bending over a woman laying on the pavement.

Forgetting her own distress, the doctor in Pari made her rush over to them.

"You fainted and hit your head," the man was saying to the woman. "But the ambulance is here now."

care about me?" Pari's lip trembled with gratitude… and hope.

"Of course I care about you. But Pari, have you been crying?"

"Manish was just using me," she admitted, wretchedly. "You must think I'm so stupid, after you warned me about him."

"I was pretty dim myself," said Jamil. "For not telling you the real reason I didn't want you to go.

"I probably shouldn't say it, because we've been friends for so long that I guess that's all you want from me. But the real reason I came here is because I couldn't watch you marry Manish before I'd told you how I really feel – which is that I love you."

She didn't know if it was a mirage… "Jamil! But what are you doing here?"

As a pair of paramedics squeezed through the crowd and took over, the man stood up and turned around.

"Jamil!" Pari didn't know if she'd stumbled into an oasis or a mirage.

"A doctor is never off duty, eh?" Jamil grinned. In his tuxedo and bow tie, Pari couldn't help thinking that he looked like James Bond.

"But what are you doing here?" Pari pulled a tissue from her purse and desperately wiped her runny make-up.

"I was worried about you." He frowned behind his glasses. "I don't know if it's true what the papers are saying about you and Manish, but it's so sudden that I want to make sure it's what you really want."

"You came all this way because you

"Oh, Jamil." Pari's eyes filled anew. "I wish you'd told me that sooner, because I thought it was you that only wanted to be friends."

"You mean… that's not all you want?" The shy doctor brightened.

She stepped into his arms, and as their lips met, Pari knew he'd always be her real life Bollywood hero. Ⓜ

ACT OF KINDNESS

When my car had a flat battery in the Waitrose car park, I asked the customer services assistant if I could use their phone. Instead, she and a colleague came out and gave me a push start!

120
Calories per
biscuit

Ginger Florentines

Ingredients (Makes 18)
- ◆ **75g butter**
- ◆ **75g caster sugar**
- ◆ **1tbsp golden syrup**
- ◆ **2tsp plain flour**
- ◆ **50g crystallised ginger, chopped**
- ◆ **50g flaked almonds**
- ◆ **40g walnut halves, coarsely chopped**
- ◆ **2tbsp candied peel**
- ◆ **40g glacé cherries, chopped**
- ◆ **1tbsp single cream**
- ◆ **50g plain chocolate, broken into pieces**

1 Preheat the oven to 180°C, Fan 160°C, Gas 4 and line 3 baking trays with baking parchment. Place the butter, sugar and golden syrup in a saucepan and slowly bring to the boil. Boil for 1min.

2 Remove from the heat and stir in the flour, chopped ginger, nuts, peel, cherries and cream. Place 6 heaped tsp of the mix onto each of the prepared trays, leaving large spaces as they will spread.

3 Bake for 8min. Remove from the oven and use a plain pastry cutter or palette knife to ease the edges into a round shape. Return to the oven for 3-4min until golden. Leave the biscuits to firm slightly and then transfer to a wire rack to cool.

4 Melt the chocolate in a small heatproof bowl over a saucepan of hot water. Leave to cool, then place in a small greaseproof paper piping bag and drizzle over the top. Leave to set, then serve. **➔ 125**

RECIPE AND FOOD STYLING: JENNIE SHAPTER PHOTOGRAPHY: JON WHITTAKER

How lovely to receive a wedding invitation – but I couldn't place the young couple at all…

By Kate Finnemore

Hello. Is that Mr Wilson? Mr Alex Wilson?"

"It is. How can I help you?"

The voice on the other end of the line was warm and friendly.

"It's about the wedding invitation –"

"That's quick. We only sent them out yesterday. Hold on. Let me get the list."

I could hear him rummaging through papers, and I smiled as I pictured a desk piled high with what my late husband would have called creative chaos.

"The thing is," I said. "This is going to sound awful, but I'm not sure why I've been invited."

"Oh?"

"I've been racking my brains all morning, ever since the postman brought the invitation, and I'm sure I don't know your son. Or your future daughter-in-law."

"You think we might have invited the wrong person."

There was amusement in his tone, and I found myself smiling again. I put him in his early fifties, about my age.

"Exactly," I said.

"Let's hope we haven't, hey. That would be most unfortunate. Ah, here it is. Could you tell me your name, please?"

come to the wedding, Mrs Monroe. She still laughs every time she thinks about that trip to Paris. It was such great fun, she says."

Paris? I'd taken groups of students to Paris on five separate occasions, but there hadn't been a Jane Brown among them. Had there?

"I'll get Jane to ring you," he said.

All at once my mind was made up. "No need. I'd like to accept your kind invitation, but to the wedding ceremony only. I won't come to the reception afterwards."

It was a spur-of-the-moment decision, but the best solution, I thought, putting the phone down. If it turned out I did know the Wilsons or the bride's family,

"You think we might have invited the wrong person." His tone was amused

"Monroe." I braced myself, as I always did. "Marilyn Monroe."

A moment's silence, then: "Well, I don't need my list to know you're on it. It's – uh – an unforgettable name."

My maiden name had been a perfectly unremarkable Walker.

"I'll ask my son to check with Jane, his fiancée –"

Hmm, so my connection had to be with the bride rather than the groom.

"– and I'll phone you back. In a couple of days' time, probably. Is that all right with you?"

"Of course," I said, and a smile lingered on my face long after the phone call had ended.

Alex Wilson rang two days later, the sound of his voice sending an unexpected whisper of pleasure down my spine.

"Jane says you've definitely got to

then I'd be there to celebrate their wedding with them. And if I didn't, well then, no harm would have been done, would it?

After all, my decision had nothing whatsoever to do with the warm, friendly tones of Alex Wilson's voice – or the image of the man the voice had conjured up.

Two months later, I remained sitting as the bride and groom led the way out of the church.

Behind them came the bride's mother, arm in arm with Alex Wilson. He spoke friendly words to the people on either side of him as he passed them, and had the warm eyes and ready smile that matched the voice I'd heard over the phone.

"And that's Alex's sister with the bride's dad," the woman sitting next to me said. "Alex's wife died four years ago, you see." ➔

"You were right, we'd sent the invitation to the wrong address. Jane sorted it. There's her Marilyn, over there," he said, indicating a woman in a lime-green dress.

"And you didn't think to tell me?"

I was amused, not annoyed, I realised.

A fractional pause. Alex glanced down at his hands, then up again. The citrus notes of his cologne drifted towards me on the light summer breeze.

"I'm sorry," he said. "Your voice intrigued me somehow. I really wanted to put a face to it."

What could I say? Hadn't I wanted to do exactly the same?

He touched his hand to my arm.

"If I've put you to any expense –"

His eyes were a rich brown. Laughter lines fanned out from the corners.

"No. Not at all."

The bride's father hurried over, looking at his watch.

"We ought to be getting along, Alex.

This time his hand remained on my arm. "You'll stay won't you, for the reception?"

How sad, I thought, *not to be there to see your own son's wedding.*

The bells pealed. The photographer took masses of photographs.

I stood outside with the others, enjoying the atmosphere and the sunshine on my face. It was a perfect, summery June afternoon.

"Someone I don't recognise. You must be Marilyn."

It was Alex Wilson, holding out a hand.

"I am," I said, smiling. His hand was warm and firm. "It's a lovely wedding. You must be very proud of your son and his new wife. But I feel I'm here under false pretences. I don't know anyone, I'm afraid."

We've got a timetable to keep to."

Alex turned to me. This time his hand remained on my arm.

"You'll stay, won't you? For the reception?"

My eyes met his, and I was conscious of the warmth of his hand on my arm.

"I will," I promised. Ⓜ

....

ACT OF KINDNESS

It was a dark autumn evening and our car had broken down on a country road in France. We were immensely grateful to the two strangers who stopped and helped, staying with us until the breakdown truck and taxi arrived.

Brain Boosters

Missing Link

The answer to each clue is a word which has a link with each of the three words listed.

This word may come at the end (eg **HEAD** linked with **BEACH, BIG, HAMMER**), at the beginning (eg **BLACK** linked with **BEAUTY, BOARD** and **JACK**) or a mixture of the two (eg **STONE** linked with **HAIL, LIME** and **WALL**).

ACROSS

1 Berry, Cheese, Poll (5)
4 Gold, Guard, Ivory (5)
7 Fisher, Prawn, Size (4)
8 Key, Mathematical, Private (8)
9 Belly, Break, Clog (6)
11 Mountain, Off, Season (4)
12 Bridle, Finder, Garden (4)
14 Gate, Ox, Wind (4)
17 Chair, Robe, Salts (4)
18 Bean, Fingers, Peanut (6)
19 Post, School, Wardrobe (8)
21 Ship, Stone, Union (4)
22 Dock, Farm, Timber (5)
23 Boat, Root, Suez (5)

DOWN

1 Bound, Galaxy, Staircase (6)
2 Doll, Time, Trade (3)
3 Biscuit, Communion, Thin (5)
4 Hall, Pianist, Rock (7)
5 Eater, Hill, Soldier (3)
6 Horse, Virus, War (6)
10 Slow, Stage, Tennis (5)
11 Finger, News, Run (5)
13 Candle, Share, Stall (7)
15 Mirror, Table, Unit (6)
16 Outlet, Therapy, Trade (6)
18 Instinct, Principles, Wage (5)
20 Coal, Jack, Mac (3)
21 Belt, Club, Oven (3)

Turn To Page 159 For Solutions

Hidden word in the shaded squares: _____

Book Club Romeo

Was Zoe's romance story really true? More importantly, would it have a happy ending?

By Patsy Collins

See you tonight, Gerri," one of the girls called as they all left the office on Friday.

"I'll be there," I promised.

"Have fun," Zoe said.

"I take it you won't be joining us?" another of the youngsters asked.

"No. I, er… well, I've got a date actually," Zoe said.

"Ooooh!" We all said that pretty much simultaneously. Zoe is the last person we'd have expected to have a hot date and her half shy, half cat's-got-the-cream smile suggested that's exactly what her evening would be. Everyone stopped their rush for freedom and clustered round Zoe hurling excited questions.

"Who is he?"

"Where are you going?"

"Have you been dating long?"

"What will you wear?"

After a moment's silence I added, "Yeah, come on, Zoe – where are you going?" I was her best, and I thought only, friend but it was the first I'd heard of this.

"Dinner and the theatre… and Sebastien said I'd be back really late."

"Oh, classy."

"Have a great time."

"We'll want the details on Monday." ➔

ILLUSTRATION: ISTOCKPHOTO

The girls were still talking about Zoe's date when we met at the pub for karaoke that evening. Everyone was pleased for her. Most also expressed surprise. No one doubted she was telling the truth, not then.

About a month before that, the younger members of staff invited me and Zoe to karaoke with them on Friday night as usual. Zoe, as she always did, refused. She did it politely, but a few had taken offence.

I hadn't joined them for the last few weeks, but there was to be a competition, which sounded like fun. I'd said I'd sing just before them, as I'm so bad they'd seem great. A bit of a backhanded compliment I realised as I said it, but they'd taken it in the spirit it was meant.

"I'll be there," I promised.

"We know you will, Gerri," was the pointed reply. "Unlike Madam 'oh but I've got a book to read' you can stand to be with us away from work."

"Oh dear, I've upset them," Zoe said, when it was just us left in the office. "I didn't mean to."

"I know you didn't," I told her as we walked down the stairs together. "But look at it from their point of view. They think they're being nice, inviting us to join them and you seem to throw it in their faces by saying you'd rather stay in and do nothing."

"I don't do nothing…"

"You read?" It was a rhetorical question. She's so obsessed with books that she even dresses like a librarian – well like the plain and buttoned up librarian we had at school, who is the only one I've actually met.

"I enjoy reading. What's wrong with that?" she pleaded.

"Absolutely nothing." Reading itself wasn't the problem, it was just that she did little else and seemed to prefer characters to most real people.

"Do you really think I'd enjoy karaoke, or be any fun to have along?"

She had a point. Not only would she hate it, but she'd put a dampener on everyone else too – if you don't fully embrace the craziness of karaoke then it shows and can seem a bit judgemental. That's why I only go when I'm really in the mood to let my hair down.

"It wasn't that you didn't want to go, it's that they knew you wouldn't be doing anything else. If you'd said you had a date they'd have been pleased for you."

"I should have lied?"

"I didn't say that but… look, you need some kind of social life. You can't just

"You need some kind of social life. You can't just work, eat, sleep and read."

walked down the stairs together. "But look at it from their point of view. They think they're being nice, inviting us to join them and you seem to throw it in their faces by saying you'd rather stay in and do nothing."

"I don't do nothing…"

"You read?" It was a rhetorical question. She's so obsessed with books that she even dresses like a librarian – well

work, eat, sleep and read."

Her look said not only that she thought she could do just that, but that was exactly what she wanted.

"If you do, you're going to end up really lonely. You need to meet people, make friends."

"But I meet people at work and you're my friend."

"I suppose."

My parents moved to a new town when I was fifteen and I started at a new school. Everyone else, except Zoe, already had friends and teachers often sat me next to her. She was really quiet, with little interest in anything but stories, but I didn't mind that. I could easily talk for two and liked an audience. She'd been a good friend, listening to my concerns, making me see there was more to life than being popular with a hectic social life, and helping me catch up on schoolwork I'd missed due to the move. We'd stayed in touch and, whenever she didn't have her

"Book club more like!" someone else responded before Zoe could answer. She didn't need to, her expression made it obvious to everyone that her evening would indeed involve a book.

I had asked her later and she admitted it. "But we don't just sit there reading. I've met quite a few people and we discuss the books and sometimes we go out together. It's a lot of fun."

Although it wasn't what I'd had in mind when I suggested she improve her social life it definitely seemed like a step in the right direction and I said so.

"You were right – I just needed to find the right sort of people," she told me

nose in a book, she'd continued helping me in her quiet way.

As I knew she was hard working and reliable I hadn't hesitated in recommending her when a vacancy opened up at work. Where the paperwork was involved she'd fully justified my confidence, but the same didn't apply to the people. I felt I owed it to her to help with that – or maybe I just wanted to stop feeling that as her only friend I was responsible for her happiness. Either way, I really didn't want the poor woman to be lonely forever. I nagged and nagged until she told me she'd joined a club. She didn't sound very keen at first, but after the first meeting she was a lot more positive – vague but positive.

"You were right – I just needed to find the right sort of people," she told me.

The next Friday, when the girls invited us to join them at karaoke, Zoe and I both said no. I gave a convincing excuse and Zoe tried…

"I've already arranged to go out tonight… to a club."

"Night club?" One girl asked.

"It hasn't helped at work though, has it? They still think I prefer books to company."

That was true. In fact most seemed to think she was the only member of her book club. More of us came round to that way of thinking when she claimed to be going to the book club on the following three Fridays.

"My mum goes to a book club, but it's only once a month," someone said.

The others agreed that every week seemed too frequent and Friday night an unlikely time to hold it. I wanted to believe Zoe, so gave her a chance to explain herself.

"You're right, the official meetings are only once a month and they're on Wednesdays."

"So what do you really do on Fridays?"

"Some of us read more than one book a month, so we meet up for coffee to talk about them. The more we have in common, reading wise, the more frequently we meet. There's one person I see most days." She blushed a little.

"Well, that's good," I said quickly, ➡

wanting to assure her I wasn't upset that she had another friend. I also knew that I wasn't the only person who would feel that way.

"No one will mind you not coming out with us because you're having a drink with a friend," I said.

I thought she'd pick up on my hint and that's how she'd phrase it the next Friday, but instead she astounded us with news of her date with Sebastien. As I said, at the time none of us doubted the truth of it. Although she was an unlikely person to have such news, she was even more unlikely to lie.

would be suitable for a romantic hero.

"How did you meet this man of yours?" I asked.

"Through the book club, of course."

Of course she did, but was he real, or a figment of either Zoe's or an author's imagination?

I asked her to describe Sebastien.

She looked momentarily confused. "Tall, dark and handsome," she eventually told me.

"Like someone from a book?"

"It depends on the book," she said. And just when I thought I was on to her, she sdded, "Would you like to see a

Sebastien wasn't handsome – he was totally, absolutely drop-dead gorgeous!

On Monday when she told me they'd gone to The Ivy in London and then to a play in the West End I was surprised. She started going into detail, but I wasn't interested in the plot and cut her short.

"That's an unusual first date."

"Oh, it wasn't the first. We went to The Round Tower in Portsmouth. There's a cafe underneath and we had Sunday lunch there a fortnight ago."

As it happens, I've been to Portsmouth and seen that café. Which also means I've seen the tower too – and recognised it when I saw it on the cover of the book she was reading at lunchtime a couple of weeks ago.

"And the next time?" I prompted.

"We went to Max Gate."

"Is that a pub?"

She'd laughed. "No, it's where Thomas Hardy lived."

Again she started to go into detail, and again I didn't listen.

Even I knew Thomas Hardy was an author. I began to wonder. Sebastien is quite an exotic sounding name, one that

photo?" She handed over her phone.

I flicked through a few group shots of people until I found one with just her and a man.

"Please tell me this is Sebastien."

"Yep, that's him. And the picture before is of… "

"The rest of the book club, obviously," I saved her from explaining, and kept my attention on the object of interest.

Sebastien wasn't handsome – he was totally, absolutely, drop-dead gorgeous! The photo was taken outside a West End theatre. His arm was around Zoe's shoulder, but it looked like a just-for-the-photo pose, not a natural gesture. Was he an actor? Was I jealous and therefore doubting my friend's relationship with that stunning man?

Zoe's dates took a weird turn after that. Or rather they'd have seemed weird had I not started flicking through each book she brought into work and seeing that everything she and Sebastien did, or the places they went, appeared in the story. I was positive not everything was as Zoe described it. I don't want to be rude about my friend, but she's quite ordinary. She has a nice personality, but it's the quiet kind. Sebastien is not only extremely good looking, but all the outlandish dates were his suggestion. If he existed… which of he did, because Zoe wasn't a liar and I'd seen a photo.

One day, I was looking at her latest book, when Zoe's bookmark fell to the floor. I wheeled my chair back to look for it, and ran over the thing, ripping it.

"What's up with you?" Zoe asked when she returned to her desk. "You look like something awful has happened."

"It's your bookmark, I'm afraid…" I held up the sad remains and noticed she'd gone white. "Please don't be upset. I'll get you another."

which I knew from an internet search is set on the Yorkshire moors.

"I'll show you," she said.

Sebastien was in some of those photos too. I got her to show them around the office, because I knew I wasn't the only one growing concerned that her boyfriend was more literary than literally true. It didn't help, because one look at that tall lean body, and incredible face, convinced everyone that he couldn't really be her boyfriend. Most were just judging by appearances, but one had more to go on.

She took me to one side and said, "I know him. He lives next door."

"And does he belong to a book club?"

"No idea, but he does have a girlfriend, and it's not Zoe."

I had to talk to her, but didn't know where to start. Her mentioning another

"Sebastien lives next door. He has a girlfriend, and it's not Zoe" she said

"What? Oh! Don't worry, I've got lots more – I get given them every birthday and Christmas." It was nice of her to be so gracious, especially as I'd briefly seen how much she cared about that particular bookmark. It was good to know she valued my friendship more.

How was Yorkshire?" I asked after her trip there, which just happened to be after she'd read *Wuthering Heights,*

trip to Portsmouth made it all the more urgent. That's where she said Sebastien took her for their first date and she was clearly very excited.

Perhaps she thought returning there was significant and the relationship she'd invented for herself was about to become more serious. Or maybe he was seeing both women. Whatever was going on, Zoe was going to get hurt.

Once she'd finished telling me ➡

Charles Dickens had lived in Portsmouth and they were going to the museum, I asked why they'd not gone on their first date.

"Sebastien's not a fan."

"But he's taking you now?"

"Yes. Well no… Sebastien isn't coming with us."

"Who? What? Eh?"

That's when I got the whole story. She'd been nervously pacing outside where the book club meet, trying to pluck up the courage to go in, when Sebastien had approached her. He was smitten with one of the members, but the woman didn't seem very interested. He hoped to persuade Zoe to help him change that.

thing they'd understand I would prefer to karaoke."

"Yeah, OK I suppose you did when you said he was taking you to the theatre. But since then, you said you met him most days and you don't do you?"

"I said I met someone from the book group – you just assumed it was Sebastien."

Maybe I had, and I'll admit I'm far better at talking to Zoe than to listening to her, so I might not have given her comments my full attention. In fact, I remembered that more than once I'd interrupted her and then felt I was missing something.

"Then who is it? Just a friend, or more than that."

"I said I met someone from the book group – you assumed it was Sebastien"

"Because I was paying attention to how she reacted to him, I forgot to be nervous and enjoyed the evening. Sebastien's idea was that I'd pretend to be his girlfriend and make her jealous, but I didn't want to do anything dishonest and didn't have too. I discovered that she, like him, wasn't much of a reader, so had some other reason to go. In her case it was boredom, so I suggested to Sebastien that he organise fun outings connected with the books we read. It worked brilliantly and they're a couple now."

"Hang on, you didn't want to behave dishonestly in front of those strangers, but have lied to me?"

"No, I haven't, not really. I just took your advice about what to say to the girls at work. Instead of saying I was on a book club trip, I made it sound like the kind of

"More. His name is Mark." She showed me a photo and flashed her shy but pleased with herself smile. "My book Mark."

Mark isn't drop dead gorgeous. He's just ordinary, except for a grin so infectious I smiled back at his image. In the picture his arm was around Zoe. It didn't look posed, it looked natural, right.

You'll have gathered I don't read many books, and so I don't know how many really end with "and they lived happily ever after", but I think Zoe's story will.

ACT OF KINDNESS

My local gardening group often dig up plants to help fill the gardens of new neighbours and during Covid lockdown distributed seeds to those who couldn't get their own.

✦ Set at Christmas time, *Gremlins* in 1984 brought us cute furry creatures that transform into evil monsters – and spawned a massive merchandising campaign!

✦ **The 1931 adaptation of *Frankenstein* was the first monster movie and the first of a long line of movies thereafter about Mary Shelley's iconic creature.**

FANCY THAT!

Fascinating facts on **Monster Movies!**

✦ **The Day of the Triffids (1962) was based on the sci-fi novel of the same name by John Wyndham, in which a meteor shower renders everyone blind as monster plants feed on them!**

✦ *The Fly* (1986) saw Jeff Goldblum accidentally fuse himself with a housefly, leaving viewers both grossed-out and dying to find out how far the transformation would go!

✦ *Jurassic Park* was first released in 1993 and has spawned an entire franchise of movies, as well as theme park rides. The T-Rex is the star but it has the scariest raptors ever seen on film!

The ultimate in alien terror.

The Thing in 1982 was an alien entity that works its way through a group of Antarctic researchers, headed up by Kurt Russell

✦ In 1987 the monsters were extra-terrestrial again when Arnold Schwarzenegger was stalked and hunted by the *Predator*. Three sequels were made, as well as a cross-over with the Alien franchise.

✦ 1999's *The Mummy* is a fun trip into 1920s Egypt, complete with plaques and the undead, all played with reckless abandon – a whole lot of family fun!

Beneath The Waves

Jane had come to this place full of happy childhood memories in the hope of gaining some inspiration

By Scott Montgomery

Jane Stephenson stood on the deserted esplanade and let childhood memories engulf her like the autumnal wind blowing in from the sea.

Way back then it had all been about that annual fortnight when school was out and an adventure at the seaside beckoned. Nothing had been more important than the imminent building of sandcastles, devouring ice-cream cones and candy floss, or the risk of chipped teeth from biting at sweet sticks of hard rock.

The young Jane had come from a small, land-locked mining town just outside of Glasgow. The escape was by train – subsequently by family car – to the coast, and to a small caravan with its gas stove and whistling kettle, cramped little bunks for kids and folding down sofa-bed for their parents.

The Scottish West Coast, with its sandy beaches and rugged landscapes was, at times, mysterious but also fun and exciting.

Kids' play parks had swings, chutes and roundabouts. Crazy golf, pitch and putt, or a funfair would come to town – bringing waltzers, ghost trains and coconut shies.

There was also the gaudy thrill of the amusement arcade. A pre-teen Jane had delighted in commandeering and gaining high scores at the Pac-Man cabinet. The game guzzled her pocket money in a similar fashion to the flashing, titular yellow character who happily chomped his way through a maze of flashing dots.

Jane was an author. She had penned several novels and supplemented her freelance lifestyle by teaching creative writing on a part-time basis at a Glasgow college. Her books, historical family sagas, were not bestsellers but they had a loyal, if small readership. Progress on the ninth volume had stalled, so Jane had deliberately decamped to this place,

display, knowing exactly who it would be. "Morning, Bella."

"How're things, dear? Settling in all right? Got yourself a 'Kiss-me-quick' hat yet?" A vaguely piggy grunt of laugher sounded in Jane's ears. "You probably should've gone somewhere warm, like Spain or Italy?"

"I like to suffer for my art."

"Indeed." Another grunt. "It sounds like it's blowing a hurricane out there. At least get in out of the cold, for goodness sake. Somewhere cosy. Preferably in front of your laptop and then you can work on a chapter or two. There's a good girl."

"I'm mind-mapping some ideas at this very moment," she told her agent

getting away from on it all in the hope that she might find her muse once more – and hopefully create something different to what she'd done before.

She could stay for one week, before her students returned for their next semester.

Jane's mobile phone buzzed in her coat pocket and she answered, not even bothering to check the caller

Bella Cartwright, Jane's kindly but weary literary agent, kept in touch each day by email or phone. She had a great deal of experience of authors and their frequently unpredictable ways.

"I'm mind-mapping some ideas at this very moment," said Jane as she started to walk along the asphalt esplanade.

"That sounds like something your ➜

students would say when they haven't actually done anything."

"Fair point. I've made a fundamental mistake that I'd be the first to criticise them for," sighed Jane. "I have a setting but no characters."

A blast of cold wind blew all around.

"What was that, darling?" the mobile phone briefly cut out. "You're breaking up."

Jane took the phone from her ear and glanced at the blank display. No signal. Bella could call back.

An ominous rumble of thunder erupted in the granite sky and the wind howled once more as the author made her way down to the beach. Seagulls squawked and swooped down from above. The sand seemed almost alive, rising up and shimmering like a fawn-coloured aurora borealis. Stray gritty grains felt rough

Vessels of different sizes were tied up at the quayside – bobbing up and down in the foamy saltwater. There were skiffs, dinghies and motorboats. Larger fishing craft were also dotted around, some new and others rusting and derelict.

Perhaps unsurprisingly, the place was nearly deserted. Jane was no sailor so presumably this was not ideal weather to be out on the ocean wave.

I have to write some of this stuff down, thought Jane. Story ideas formed in her mind like the big droplets of rain that were starting to fall. She would scribble some notes whenever she got the chance. For now, though, she didn't want her precious notebook to get blown away.

Beyond the harbour was a wooden jetty that stretched out into the sea. Jane squinted and could make out the shape of

The old man's manner was reassuring; as if he were from a bygone era

against her face as she ploughed on, half-expecting some kind of mythical Egyptian creature to materialise out of thin air, like Anubis, the jackal-headed God of the Dead.

When Jane managed to catch a breath the air was tinged with the reek of fresh seaweed, clumps of which lay dotted around in glistening, rubbery heaps along the shore. Nearer the water, the writer's feet sank a little in the damp sand as she struggled on. Her ears were filled with the sound of the relentless attack of ocean foam and spray as it continued its eternal surge against the land. In that moment the sea truly seemed like a living, breathing beast, a menacing leviathan from the deep.

On she trekked, enjoying the bracing air. The sand eventually gave way to pebbles and then rocks. Heading back up onto the concrete promenade, it soon wound towards a small, working harbour.

a lone figure standing on the narrow wooden pier.

Worried that the person could potentially be in danger, she moved closer, quickening her step as best she could.

Soon the figure became more distinct. It was a man aged about sixty and he had a nautical air about him. Dressed in a scruffy waterproof jacket, faded denims and Wellington boots, he was fairly rotund. A full head of untidy white hair spilled out from underneath his hat. He gazed at the horizon, air and sea both so grey as to be almost identical.

"Ahoy there!" Jane said loudly, not wishing to sneak up on him.

The old man turned around. Momentarily taken aback, he frowned. Then he doffed his cap. "Can I help you, missus?" His voice was mellifluous, polite.

"Sorry if I disturbed you," said Jane.

"It's a bit blowy, so I just wanted to make sure you were OK."

His craggy features creased into a pleasant smile. "Why, I'm fine, madam. Thank you for looking out for an old man." He gestured behind him with a callused hand. "But you're right. Perhaps we should head back in. I'm William, by the way."

Something about this quiet gentleman's old-fashioned manner was reassuring; as if he were from a bygone era.

"Jane." She shivered slightly, running a hand through her damp hair. "I don't know about you, William, but I'm really cold. Do you fancy a cuppa?"

The town itself had seen better days. Clothing boutiques, a bookseller, several restaurants, were empty, adorned with "To Let" signage at best, or ruined at worst. Graffiti-covered metal shutters clanked in the breeze. Charity shops had taken over, apart from chain brands of pharmacy, supermarket and coffee shops, all of which were a familiar presence on high streets up and down the country.

Near the unkempt pitch and putt green was Tee for Two, a traditional tea room that, aside from a terrible punning name and the need for a coat of paint, looked inviting, so Jane and her new companion went inside.

Small tables were covered in red and white gingham cloths, with white plastic placemats and cutlery stacked in stainless steel flagons. Tomato ketchup and brown sauce bottles were lined up alongside other condiments like salt, pepper and vinegar. Laminated menus offered calorie-filled delights of full Scottish breakfasts or lighter fare of toasted tea cakes and fruit scones.

They sat at a two-seat table that wobbled every time Jane leant on it.

"Would you like a latte, cappuccino, espresso? A flat white?" quizzed the author.

The quiet sailor looked baffled. "Erm…"

"Tea?"

"Something I've heard of. Yes, please."

"I'll have the same."

A slim waitress in her mid-thirties came over. She had auburn hair tied back in a ponytail and was dressed in black trousers and a white blouse. "What can I get you?" A name-tag on her identified her as Sheila.

"Tea, for two, please," said Jane, taking off her coat and draping it behind her chair.

"Coming right up." Sheila gave a smile in Jane's direction but seemed to ignore William as she turned on her heel to fetch the refreshments.

Although Jane had come out to the little coastal town intent on isolating herself, she was fascinated by the elderly seaman. At the table, William seemed to come to life.

Apart from a spell of compulsory National Service in the Merchant Navy, he had always been a fisherman, helping his father on the family boat ever since he had been old enough to leave school at 14. In the 1960s there had much more of a fishing industry, he had declared wistfully.

Jane listened, jotting down notes as the old character didn't seem to mind. *Funny,* thought Jane, *he never touches his tea, while I seem to be drinking it all.*

The next day, down at the esplanade on another early constitutional, Jane noticed William once more. "Hello again, I was ➤

just thinking about you," said the writer.

"Good morning," He smiled. "How delightful to see you again."

They ambled along together, with Jane slowing her pace as the old man struggled to keep up with her. "How about a breather?" He gasped.

It was almost like having déjà vu, being back in Tee for Two with this kindly old man of the sea, pondered Jane. "I really don't mean to pry, William…" she said.

"But?"

"If I can ask you a personal question…" stammered Jane. "You are a lovely man but you seem so sad… lonely. Can I ask why?"

"Very perceptive of you. Yes, I am lonely. But more specifically, I am alone. I'm a widower and Jacob, my only son, is also gone, lost at sea many years ago."

"I'm sorry to hear that."

"It was an accident. Our boat was swept onto jagged rocks in a freak gale that somehow eluded the weather forecasts. We would never have been out in it if we'd known." William gave a weak smile. "He has a grave, empty of course, but I rarely visit it apart from putting fresh flowers there on his birthday. Instead I go down to the water's edge every day. I like to think of him being at peace. He loves the sea." His deep voice faltered for a moment. "He *loved* the sea. That's one of the worst things about losing someone…"

Jane frowned in sympathy, nodding for him to continue.

"Referring to them in the past tense. Knowing you will never see them again. It's so final."

Jane felt tears misting her vision so she rubbed at her eyes. "Excuse me one moment, William." She rose, heading to the counter. "I'll just get the bill."

"Oh, please, no. I feel very

ungentlemanly," he called after her, his voice had regained some of its earlier cheer. "Letting a lady pay."

"Not at all. It's the least I can do. You've been such lovely company." This tactic gave the emotional author a brief moment that she needed to compose herself a little.

Sheila, the waitress, was absentmindedly tapping away at a mobile phone. Looking up, she set

it aside. "Have you been stood up again, love?"

"Beg your pardon?" Jane's brow furrowed in puzzlement.

"Y'know, the way you've been in here the last couple of days all on your lonesome with a big pot of tea for two."

"But I was just talking to…" Whirling round, she looked at her table and gasped.

It was empty. Apart from her pen, notebook, the teapot and two mugs, one of which was clearly untouched.

"I mean obviously I guessed you were a writer, the way you were talking to yourself and scribbling away. JK Rowling used to write in cafes too. Suppose that's how you come up with the characters on so on?" She grinned. "Feel free to put me in your next book!" the waitress said with a smile.

Jane reciprocated with what she hoped was also a smile although it felt more like a confused grimace.

"Thank you. We've – I mean… I've enjoyed coming here." She rummaged around in her purse. Extracting a crumpled £20 note, she smoothed it out and handed it over. "Keep the change."

"Oh, that's very decent of you!" The waitress practically had to shout over the sound of the chugging, hissing espresso machine. "Thanks. Bye-bye."

"Take care. Cheerio." Jane gathered up her notebook and pen. The bewildered author ventured out onto the street and was immediately drawn towards the promenade, unable to resist the urge to return there.

from her handbag and flicked through the pages of scribbled jottings about a tragic, melancholy old sailor.

He had seemed so real.

The mobile rang again a few minutes later and this time Jane tapped the green reply icon on the display screen and held the phone to her ear. "Hi, Bella."

Her agent's voice seemed to echo through the mist. "How goes it, dear? I hope you've found a Candyfloss stall?"

"Well, not one that'll open until about Easter." Jane knew that Bella's feeble attempt at small talk was her way of skirting around the burning question that she was desperate to know the answer to but too apprehensive to ask.

"I'm not sure you're going to like the

She flicked through her notes about the old sailor… he had seemed so real…

Mist swirled around the air, mingling with her visible breaths as she trudged along the sand, which gave way to the small pebbles underfoot, signalling the uneven pathway to the small harbour.

Then she saw him. That instantly recognisable maritime figure. Kindly yet enigmatic. Familiar yet mysterious. He was standing at the jetty – shuffling towards the water's edge.

"William! Wait! Stop!" Jane rushed towards the retreating figure.

The old man turned, smiled and gave a slow, friendly wave.

Then he disappeared.

Unnerved, Jane blinked in surprise and stood silently, wrapping her arms around herself, feeling a sudden chill.

The quiet was fragmented by the shrill ringing tone of the mobile phone in her coat pocket. She nearly jumped in fright and let it go to voicemail.

Jane fished the ever-present notebook

sound of this," Jane said coolly, making a decision. "But trust me. I'm abandoning the series for now."

"What?" There was a nervous gulp at the other end of the phone. "That's a big step, darling."

"I know," the writer conceded. "But don't worry. I've already decided on a replacement book."

Those words were instant music to the agent's ears. "Gosh, good show."

Jane allowed herself a smile. "That new direction I want to branch into – how do you feel about a ghost story…?" MW

ACT OF KINDNESS

When lockdown hit in 2020, my wife and I wanted to help our elderly neighbours. We were glad to assist with running errands to the pharmacy and supermarket, and paying bills on their behalf.

Where The Heart Is...

Love can blind us to the imperfections of a new home – and that can be rather a good thing

By Lin Silver

1988

Laura squeezed John's hand tightly with excitement. They were sitting in the car in the car park opposite Blackgate Road.

"That's number 49," Laura said, pointing to a particular house in a row of similar, admittedly rather run-down, terraced homes. "So the flat upstairs is 49A. What do you think?"

"Looks good to me," John said, with his gorgeous smile. "The windows at the front must be the living room."

"Quite cosy," Laura said, her imagination flying away with her. "Snuggled up in a nice little flat, while the world goes by…"

John laughed. "Well, it's certainly an improvement on my grotty bed-sit."

"There's nothing grotty about your bed-sit," Laura murmured, stroking his hand, as she thought of all the happy times they'd spent together in that one room since finding each other and falling deeply in love.

"Suppose not," John replied. "But then again a bit more privacy would be nice."

It was true that his landlady, who also lived on the premises, was a bit of a nuisance – as was not being able to get into the bathroom when you needed it.

"Come on, then," he said, flinging the car door open and sliding his long, skinny legs out from under the wheel of the old Volvo. It was ten years old, a yucky beige colour spotted with rust. But it was fine to drive.

When they knocked on the door of number 49, it was answered by a scruffy-looking couple who obviously inhabited the downstairs.

"We've come about the flat," Laura said with a smile.

"OK," said the woman, stubbing out her cigarette on the doorstep and not bothering to pick up the butt. "Landlord's not here yet. Must've got held up in the traffic. But door's open, so you might as well have a look."

In truth, the bedroom was neither big nor lovely but they were madly in love

"Thanks," said John and Laura, heading up the stairs with a badly worn carpet.

The main room was indeed the one that overlooked the car park. Laura lifted one of the tatty net curtains and pulled a face.

"Well, it would definitely need new curtains!" she declared.

"Or don't have any," John replied. "We can put the sofa right here and sit and watch all the traffic coming and going across the road."

"Sounds like fun," Laura giggled, landing him a playful punch.

"I can think of better fun to have here," he retorted, sweeping her into his arms and twirling her round. They both laughed. They were both so much in love.

The bathroom was a bit abysmal but John said straight away that he could tidy it up and put a shower over the bath. The kitchen needed just about everything, but it did have the advantage of a back door you could open to access or exit via a rather creaky wooden staircase.

John pointed out that at least with it being empty, he could slap some tiles on the walls before they bought a cooker.

"Oh, look at this lovely big bedroom!" Laura sighed, opening the final door. In truth, the bedroom was neither big or lovely, but to a young couple madly in love, it was heaven on earth.

Then the landlord turned up.

"Seventy pounds a week. It is near the town centre and rail station," he said.

"Yes, we're aware of that," John replied, as the sound of a train pulling into the nearby station made its presence felt.

"We'll take it," Laura said without a second thought.

They handed over a deposit, and off they went to celebrate finding their first, wonderful new home…

2020

John was tired. "Post," he mumbled, as a pile of letters came crashing through the door.

"Half a dozen from the estate agents," he added, as he picked them up and began sifting through them. He gave Laura a cynical look. "Shall I just put those in the bin?"

Laura shrugged. She was also tired – house-hunting was tiring, not to mention frustrating.

They needed to move from the large house they'd moved into ten years ago. Their sons had homes and families of their own now, the huge garden that had seemed a good idea at the time had become a nuisance, and five bedrooms were just not needed any more.

Down-sizing was the thing to do, all their friends said. A nice little flat or maisonette with a pocket-handkerchief sized garden and a small drive on which to park their titchy but highly economical and eco-friendly car.

"May as well have a look," she said, her voice sounding as uninterested as she felt. She knew John was annoyed with her, and she also knew why. They'd viewed countless properties in the past six months, and none of them had ever been right or suited her. Most she'd dismissed as "dumps" (that was being kind) and there was ➤

always some problem. "How will the sideboard fit in with that chimney breast?" was an example.

Listlessly, she began shuffling through the leaflets and brochures. Then suddenly, she wasn't listless any more. The place in the picture spread in front of her was unrecognisable, yet she'd recognised it immediately.

The Blackgate Road area had obviously undergone total refurbishment and where the old terraces had once stood were now sleek, inviting apartments. Gone, too, was the old car park – in its place a nice recreational park with greenery and seating.

Laura had no idea how long she sat staring at the pictures, but it was obviously quite a while because she suddenly heard John asking, "Are you all right, love?"

"Yes, yes, I'm fine," she murmured, shoving the leaflet out of sight and crumpling it up. "I – I've just been thinking – I've been a bit of an idiot since we started house-hunting, haven't I? Always going on about stuff that doesn't matter, like where's this and that going to go. And I was just suddenly recalling that little place we looked at last week – you know, the one with the old-fashioned windows and low beams – and remembering how you really liked it…"

John looked surprised.

"Yes, but you didn't," he reminded her, a touch acidly. "The old style was precisely what put you off. I remember you moaning about how ridiculous all our contemporary furniture would look!"

Moaning? thought Laura, with a sharp pang in the heart. Oh dear, she certainly was going to put this right.

"Well, I've changed my mind," she announced. "Ring the estate agent now and find out if it's been sold yet. I think we should make an offer."

"Oh, love!"

She suspected there were tears in John's eyes as he came across and gave her the biggest hug in the world. The old fire still flickered.

There were certainly tears welling in her eyes as John dialled the number.

It was seeing that old Blackgate Road area again that had brought it all back to her – how, back then, she would have lived anywhere just so long as it meant she and John would live together. Who cared about trivial things like furnishings and décor? It was the person you lived with that mattered.

Somehow, over the passage of time, she'd become preoccupied with interior design and all the latest home ranges. None of that was important – being with the person you loved was what made a house a home, not having the newest cooker.

The day they'd moved into 49A, it had felt like living in paradise. Now thanks to that leaflet and the flashback it had given her, she knew she could – and would – feel that way again.

"It's still on the market!" John said as he put down the phone, excitement in his voice. "They said we can go and have another look tomorrow, if we want."

"We want," Laura assured him, getting to her feet to hug him. "Oh yes, we want!" Ⓜ

Brain Boosters

Sudoku 1   Sudoku 2

Fill in each of the blank squares with the numbers 1 to 9, so that each row, each column and each 3x3 cell contains all the numbers from 1 to 9.

Sudoku 1

		6	4		9	1		
	9			7			8	
5			7		3			2
		8				3		
	3	9	1		2	4	7	
				4				
		7		3		8		
		1	5		6	2		

Sudoku 2

				3				
2	6		7			8		
	4	3	1				7	
9	3							
	8					3	4	7
6	5					2		
		7	6		2	1	3	
		4			8		9	

Word Wheel

Turn To Page 159 For Solutions

You have ten minutes to find as many words as possible using the letters in the wheel. Each word must be three letters or more and contain the central letter. Use each letter once and no plurals, foreign words or proper nouns are allowed. There is at least one nine-letter word.

Average: 30 words
Good: 31-50 words
Excellent: 51+ words

Free At Last

It had been an unusual idea for a day out together – and one in which Sarah got more than she bargained for!

By Carrie Hewlett

"Take me *where*?" Sarah exclaimed. "To visit a decommissioned prison," Paul reiterated, giving her a self-satisfied look, pleased with himself for having thought of the idea. "It closed in 1991. I thought it would be fascinating to look round it together. There's been restoration work, but parts of the place have been left exactly how it used to be."

Sarah and her husband had agreed they wanted to spend more quality time together, but an afternoon looking round a prison wasn't exactly her idea of a great day out. "But why a prison?"

"Well, I know how much you like history. You've always got your nose said. "This is a fascinating place, with a rich history. You'll be able to explore and imagine what life would have been like for our prisoners both in the recent past as well as right back in the 1900's. Right. This prison was first opened in 1855…"

Hearing Mason talk as he showed them round, Sarah felt her arms break out in goose-bumps. Their footsteps clattering on the hard floor sent an eerie echo round the building. The beige paint on the walls only adding to the feeling of bleakness, as did the metal corridor above, which hung above their heads like a metal shroud. There was a strong fetid smell too. She wrinkled her nose. "Can you smell that?" she asked, grabbing Paul's hand. The whole place was giving her the creeps.

An afternoon looking round an old prison wasn't her idea of a great day out

stuck in a historical novel. And this is a historical building, so…" He gave her that *obvious really* stare, the one when he was being logical and she was missing the point. Though they'd been married over forty years, and she loved him dearly, it always irked her when he did that.

Still, it would be somewhere different, and, to be fair, she did like soaking up a bit of yesteryear.

"I'm glad everyone's wrapped up warm, as it's as cool inside as it is out," Mason, their bespectacled fifty-something guide

"It's like something's gone off."

Paul shook his head. "It must be your imagination."

Sarah screwed up her face and sniffed again. There was a definite weird odour. Why did Paul not smell it? Oh, Wait… she remembered that her husband's sense of smell had never been as good as hers. She glanced around to see if anyone else had noticed, but nobody looked as if they had. Or if they had, it wasn't bothering them.

Listening to Mason, and looking round, Sarah had to admit that he was right. It was a fascinating place. How on earth ➡

did people manage to survive in such cramped conditions? Some of the cells were so tiny, with just a metal framed bed, toilet and small sink squashed in. Against the backdrop of the stark walls, it must have been a depressing experience.

A shiver ran down her back at the thought of prisoners locked up in the dreadful conditions, no hope of release.

"Gawd, your hand is freezing," Paul whispered, giving it a rub. "It's some place, huh? Over two hundred years old."

Sarah nodded. Much as she hadn't been keen on being shown around an old prison, it was an eye-opening experience. And it was nice walking hand in hand with her husband. She'd always felt safe with her small hand enveloped in his. It reminded her of their courting days. She gave a faint smile. Hopefully now Paul was retired, they'd spend more time on days out and weekends away. That is if she could tear him away from the footie!

"The prison was damaged during a fire in 1906 when there was growing prisoner discontent," Mason continued. "It was also used as a military prison during both world wars."

It was as they were exiting one of the small cells, Sarah noticed that one of her shoe-laces was undone. "I'll catch up," she said, gesturing to Paul. As she stood, she caught a slight movement out of the corner of her eye. Quickly looking round, she saw a lonesome figure staring at her. Her hand flew to her face, before she gave a nervous laugh. "Oh, you made me jump! Nice costume, though," she grinned,

feeling her heartrate returning to normal.

But the figure continued to stare at her with strange eyes. Just looking at him made Sarah's stomach turn; his gaze was filled with icy hostility. But it was more than that. She blinked, realising that the prisoner's expression held signs of desperation. Like he would do anything. *anything* just to escape.

She'd no idea where he'd come from as she was sure he hadn't been there before. It must be some way of surprising visitors. In fact, the more she thought about it, the more she remembered seeing something in the pamphlet about actors portraying prisoners to make the place more realistic. Weird she hadn't seen any others floating about though. Maybe there were more as the tour continued?

"The prisoner back there was very realistic," she commented to Mason as she caught up to the others. "Suitably intimidating."

She saw him give her a bemused look. "What prisoner?"

"In the cell we just looked at. Gave me a fright as he seemed to appear out of nowhere. I presume some sort of hidey hole? He was dressed in old fashioned prison uniform. I thought he was part of the prison experience."

Mason shook his head in puzzlement. "We don't have anyone dressing up today as far as I know. What did he look like?"

Sarah furrowed her brow in concentration. "Dirty black and white trousers and top, with what looked like arrows on it with a small hat on his head. Sort of so high." She waved a hand in the

air. "Looked like a wiry character, a bit smaller than me." She continued narrowing her eyes trying to dredge her memory as it had only been a quick look. "Sandy coloured hair and odd eyes. Sort of dark and foreboding. Really, really dark. Like black holes." She rubbed her arms protectively. "Gave me the creeps."

"Hmm. Sounds like the Broad Arrow uniform, as it was known. From your description he sounds like one of our resident ghosts." Mason turned to the rest of the visitors. "Yes, lady and gentleman. We do have ghosts here, and this lady has by the sounds of it been lucky enough to

Could no one else see him? It felt like the prisoner's eyes were boring a hole right through her. "That was his nickname. Don't ask me how I know, but I do."

"But there's no one there," a bookish looking man exclaimed.

"But he was standing, right there…" Sarah felt her voice falter. This was ridiculous. Two pink spots of colour stained her cheeks. Surely someone had seen him too? Seeing the looks she was getting from the rest of the party she decided that maybe discretion was the better part of valour and she'd keep her mouth shut from now on.

The man seemed so real. Surely ghosts weren't so solid looking?

see one, so keep your eyes peeled."

A few members of the party gave a titter while glancing nervously about. But Sarah frowned. The man had seemed very real. Surely ghosts weren't so solid looking? Mason had to be winding everyone up for added show.

"There's some pictures of inmates on display towards the exit," Mason continued, "maybe you'll recognise him. Now ladies, and gentlemen, carrying on with our tour…"

Sarah's eyes suddenly widened. She raised one hand, pointing to someone just behind the others. "Doomsday!"

"Sarah, stop it," Paul said under his breath giving her an embarrassed look.

"But, he's behind you," Sarah raised a shaky finger, pointing towards Mason.

As the tour concluded, she zoomed in on the old photos, desperate to prove her point. Finally recognising a face in one of the old photographs, she nudged Paul's arm in triumph. "That's him!"

"Evil looking fellow," Paul raised a brow. He pointed to the wording under the picture. "But look how long ago this was taken."

"That was the man I saw," Sarah said firmly.

"Ahh. I know who you mean now," Mason interjected, having joined them. "That's Dark Eyed David, aka the voice of doom. He'd give out warnings of dread to the rest of the prison. Nobody took any notice of him. They just thought he was a doomsayer. He was always trying to escape, but failing. Then one night he ➤

yelled from his cell that there was going to be a fire and everyone had to get out."

"What happened?" Sarah asked. It was definitely the man she had seen.

"It was the fire of 1906. A nasty event." Mason shook his head in sorrow. "Dark Eyed David was shouting and shouting for everyone to get out. Banging on his cell door, he was, causing a right rumpus."

"Then what?" Paul interjected.

"One of the warders smelt smoke and realised there really was a fire. It was started by one of the other prisoners. Anyway, so the legend goes, this warder let out the alarm, but by then the place

Gathering outside, they waited, scanning the small windows of the prison. Thankfully they didn't have to wait too long before Mason appeared at their side.

"All OK now. False alarm. Just as well we'd finished the tour. Thank you all for coming." He glanced over to Sarah and Paul. "Maybe the doomsayer is still causing a commotion."

Sarah went to look at Paul, before realising that she was looking into a pair of dark, foreboding eyes. Looking down, instead of holding her husband's hand, as she'd thought, she was gripping Dave's!

Gasping in shock she pulled away.

Sarah realised that she was looking into a pair of dark, foreboding eyes

was filling with smoke and some of the prisoners couldn't be rescued. Terrible thing. Dark Eyed Dave was among the dead. If only they'd listened to him."

"That's terrible," said Sarah. "But I wonder why he appeared to me today?"

"I've no idea," Mason said. "Perhaps he was trying to escape again.

Suddenly they heard the smoke alarm go off and Mason quickly ushered them all out, calling over his shoulder. "If everyone could please follow me."

Sarah grabbed Paul's arm, her face white. "That's why he appeared to me. Dark Eyed Dave was warning us to get out. He must have known there was going to be a fire."

"How would he know?" Paul queried. "He didn't set it, did he?"

"Don't be daft, and I don't know." Sarah glared at him.

"What is it?" Paul asked appearing at her side. "You're as white as a sheet and look like you've seen another ghost."

Sarah gave a shiver before glancing at her husband, knowing he wouldn't believe her even if she tried. "Oh, nothing. I think I've just been spooked by this whole experience. Let's go home."

Turning back, she saw Dave nod his head and raise his hand in farewell before he loped off, fading into a mere glimmer. He'd got his freedom in the end. He'd just needed a helping hand to escape – hers. ⓂⓌ

ACT OF KINDNESS

A few years ago when I broke my wrists, I was grateful to my kind family and friends for being there, but most especially my brother and lovely neighbour who popped in daily.

102
Calories per
biscuit

RECIPE AND FOOD STYLING: JENNIE SHAPTER PHOTOGRAPHY: JON WHITTAKER

Cardamom And Orange Biscuits

Ingredients (Makes 28)

- ◆ **10 cardamom pods**
- ◆ **150g butter, cut into pieces**
- ◆ **100g golden caster sugar**
- ◆ **1 egg, lightly beaten**
- ◆ **1tbsp grated orange rind**
- ◆ **225g plain flour**
- ◆ **Strips of finely pared orange rind, to decorate**
- ◆ **125g icing sugar**
- ◆ **2tbsp orange juice**

1. Preheat the oven to 190°C, Fan 170°C, Gas 5. Lightly grease 2 baking trays. Remove the seeds from the cardamom pods and crush, using a pestle and mortar.

2. In a bowl, cream the butter and sugar together until pale and fluffy. Mix in the egg and grated orange rind. Add the flour and knead to a firm dough. Wrap and chill for 20min.

3. Roll out the dough on a lightly floured surface until 6mm thick. Using an 8cm fluted cutter, cut into rounds. Then cut into two using the same cutter, to make crescents and ovals. Re-roll the trimmings and cut more.

4. Lift on to the prepared trays and bake for 11-13min, until golden. Transfer to a wire rack to cool.

5. Gently press the pared orange rind between two sheets of kitchen paper, to remove any excess moisture. Sift the icing sugar into a bowl and mix in sufficient orange juice to make a fairly thick icing. Spread over the biscuits and sprinkle with the strips of pared orange rind. Leave to set, and serve. ➜ **139**

That Green Chiffon Scarf

It held so many happy memories of a past love…
but could it bring that love back together again?

By Jenny Worstall

I open the door of my wardrobe and rummage around for ten minutes until I find what I'm looking for.

"There you are," I say. "I knew you'd be in here somewhere, slithering about."

There was a time when I wore this constantly. A time I was fond of remembering, a special time.

I think back to the first day I ever saw it, when I was out with my best friend Gemma, browsing through Greenwich Market, one of our favourite haunts on a Saturday afternoon…

Would you look at that handbag?" Gemma said. "Isn't it beautiful?"

"That's a vintage Kelly bag," the lady behind the stall said.

"May I peek inside?" Gemma asked.

all its treasures.

"Look at these," I said. "Aren't they lovely? Look how small the waists are."

"Gorgeous!" Gemma said. "I can never resist a fifties dress. What lovely full skirts – and those prints."

"Got some great scarves," the man on the stall said. "Good price too; won't break the bank."

I picked out a beautiful long pale green chiffon scarf with a faded snakeskin print. It was snagged in a few places and the label was hanging off, but that's what you'd expect from a vintage stall. It was nothing I couldn't sort out with a needle and thread and a bit of patience. Besides, clothes with a bit of history were more interesting in my book. I tried it on; it was long enough for me to drape a couple of times around my neck and still have plenty of material flowing down.

The vintage scarf from the market stall became part of my life from then on

"Of course," the lady said. "They're very desirable, so if you're interested…"

Gemma gasped as she looked at the price tag. "Thank you," she said. "I'll have a think about that."

We continued our way through the market, marvelling at

"It suits you," Gemma said. "You look very elegant."

"I'll take it, thank you," I said to the young man. He wrapped it in soft tissue paper from under the stall.

I can honestly say that the green chiffon scarf became part of my ➡

ILLUSTRATION: SHUTTERSTOCK

life from then on. It seemed to go with so many outfits, right through the year, whether I was dressing up or down.

I was wearing it the first time I met Jamie, when Gemma and I were out on one of our jaunts around London. We had decided to walk along the Southbank, taking in the sights, then we thought we'd try the London Eye. The queue was massive and so naturally we got talking to a couple of lads who were also waiting. We all ended up standing in the same pod, overwhelmed at the sights around us. It was a clear day and we could see right across the city and beyond, with the river glinting below us.

I think it was Jamie who suggested we stroll along the Embankment afterwards, and his friend Tim who suggested we stopped for hot dogs. When Jamie asked for my phone number at the end of the afternoon, my scarf floated up in the wind as I put my number into his phone.

"Your scarf is the same green as your eyes," he said. "Beautiful."

I wore the scarf the first time Jamie and I went out to dinner. He teased me about the snakeskin print, saying I was a dangerous woman to tangle with, asking did I speak with a forked tongue and making endless jokes about creeping along, and all that sort of nonsense.

As I stand here in my bedroom and hold the scarf up to the light, I sigh. It's a little more shabby than I remember – and is that a hole I can see? Perhaps the moths have been having a nibble, I wonder. Inspecting the material closely, I can see that it is more of a tiny tear than a hole. Ah, I think, I know exactly when that happened.

It was on a bright and sunny day, when Jamie and I decided to go for a picnic. We met in Dulwich Park and strolled around chatting endlessly, getting to know one other.

"Look at the cyclists," I said. "Doesn't that look fun?"

"What sort of bicycles are they?" Jamie asked. "Those people look so relaxed, reclining like that."

"I don't know what the proper name is, but we call them banana bikes," I said. "You can hire them over there. Shall we…?"

"Why not," Jamie said. "Let's go for it."

Soon we were speeding round the park on banana bikes, having the time of our lives. Steering was a challenge as we were so close to the ground, but we managed without crashing into each other too much. Then we decided to have a race.

"Last one to the big tree there is the loser!" I cried out.

"Don't think you can beat me, Snake Woman," Jamie shouted back.

"Ah, my legs!" I said. "I'm not sure I can last much longer. I feel as if my muscles are on fire!"

"Mine too," Jamie said, laughing. "It's been nearly an hour, so we should be taking the bikes back now anyway."

"Great!" I said. "That means it's time for our picnic."

Once we had returned the bikes, we sat under the spreading trees munching our way through egg sandwiches, tomato salad, miniature pork pies and strawberries.

"This is the life," Jamie sighed sinking down into the grass. "Why does food taste more delicious when you're outside?"

"Don't know," I said, "but it's definitely true. Oh look – one strawberry left. Fight you for it?"

"You'll lose," Jamie said, snatching it out of my hand and dangling it above my head, just out of reach – or so he thought.

"Got it!" I cried in triumph, as I snatched it from his grasp and quickly popped it into my mouth before he could recapture the luscious fruit.

"I've got no chance of winning a battle with a snake, a snake in the grass," Jamie said sorrowfully.

"Never mind," I said. "There's a lovely café over by the lake. Fancy a cuppa?"

"Don't mind if I do," Jamie said.

While we sat on one of the wooden

lovely soft yellow colour for his kitchen and now I was helping him to paint the walls. I sort of hoped that one day it might be my kitchen too, but looking back I can see I was probably jumping the gun.

Jamie was using a roller to paint the main sections of the walls and I was using a brush to finish off the trickier bits like around the light switches and other nooks and crannies the roller was too wide for. We had some music on while we were painting and as the rhythms got livelier, so we painted less carefully and, during a particularly wild song, my brush flew into the air before splatting on the floor, depositing a blob of yellow on my scarf on its way down.

"Woah!" Jamie said. "Watch it! I'll put on some slower music now I think."

He set his iPod to play a love ballad

I kneel on the floor of my bedroom as the scarf brings back so many memories

benches outside the café, Jamie pointed at the little rip in my scarf.

"Did you catch it on the bicycle?" he asked me.

"Must have," I replied. "Or maybe when you were trying to steal the last strawberry?"

"What a shame," he said.

"Not at all," I replied. "It's going to remind me of a lovely afternoon."

It really was a perfect afternoon, I think, kneeling on the floor of my bedroom in front of the wardrobe. I inspect the scarf even more closely. Yes, the little touch of yellow paint is still visible, just there at the end, next to the label. Now that brings back some more happy memories…

Perhaps it was silly to wear the scarf while we were decorating but I just forgot to take it off. I had helped Jamie choose a

and we painted on with more restrained movements, pausing only to give each other soppy looks out of the corners of our eyes.

"You know I like you, don't you?" Jamie observed.

"I had no idea," I joked.

"You're quite a girl," Jamie said gruffly as he got the ladder out and started doing the ceiling.

"Careful!" I said. "Mine you don't get paint in your hair – oops, too late! You actually look very fetching with that yellow streak."

"Why, thank you kindly," Jamie said. "Would you like one? To match the blob on your scarf?"

I hold the scarf close to me as I sit in my bedroom, then run my finger over the yellow paint. I could have washed it ➤

out, I suppose, but it means too much to me.

Shortly after the kitchen painting episode, Jamie received a job offer to go and work in the States for a year, something he had always wanted to do and indeed had worked very hard to achieve, but something he had never mentioned to me, in case it didn't work out he said.

"We must keep in touch," Jamie said. "I hope you know I'm very fond of you."

However, a long distance relationship is a very difficult thing and I didn't want to hear that he was merely fond of me, I wanted him to declare himself and ask me to wait for him.

After a few sad months I gave up hoping. I emailed Jamie and told him I thought it was best if we didn't contact each other again and that maybe we should feel free to see other people. I heard nothing back from him for a long time after that.

Sitting in my bedroom, I pick at a loose thread on the rolled edge of the scarf. It was beginning to unravel just as our romance had unravelled.

Gemma encouraged me during that long year to go out with her and to meet new people but my heart wasn't in it. I just couldn't forget Jamie. I thought of ringing or emailing him again many times while he was away but thought I had no right to do so after saying we should break things off. What a mess; I handled everything so badly. That was when the scarf was banished to the back of the wardrobe. I couldn't face wearing it again, with all its associations.

I wind the scarf around my neck and stand in front of the mirror, tidying away the bit with the loose thread, but making sure the blob of kitchen paint and the little hole from the bike ride can be seen. I smile. Jamie will be here very soon. He has finished his year abroad and rang me last night from the airport.

"Is it all right to talk?" he asked. "You must say straight away if you don't want to. You have no idea how much I've missed you – you and your snake scarf! I should have had the courage to tell you before I left – I'm in love with you, have been for a very long time – but I didn't want you to feel you had to wait for me."

"Well, I waited anyway," I said. "And I feel the same, by the way… you know, about the love bit."

"Say it!" Jamie said.

"I love you," I said. "Sorry I made a mess of things…"

"Sorry I was too timid to say how I felt…" Jamie said.

"Shall I come round and see you tomorrow?" he asked.

"Yes please," I said.

So here I am, waiting for him, wearing my beautiful long pale green chiffon scarf with the delicate snakeskin pattern, complete with battle scars and history, waiting for Jamie, for my love. I'm looking forward to embracing the future together, whatever life throws our way. **MW**

ACT OF KINDNESS

During a lockdown gardening session, I left spare plants on my front wall for passers-by. Next time I looked, there was a box of chocolates with a note saying, "Thank you!"

Brain Boosters

Kriss Kross

Try to fit all the listed words back into the grid.

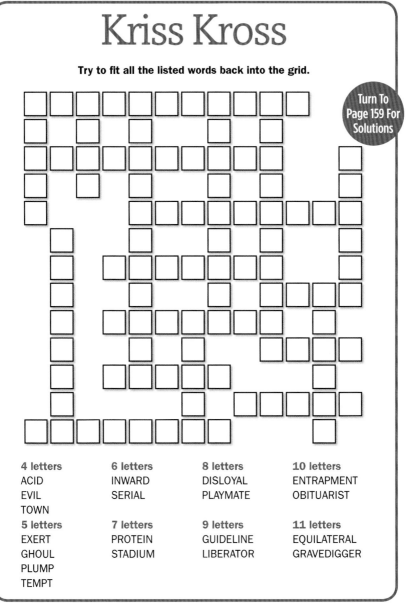

Turn To Page 159 For Solutions

4 letters
ACID
EVIL
TOWN

5 letters
EXERT
GHOUL
PLUMP
TEMPT

6 letters
INWARD
SERIAL

7 letters
PROTEIN
STADIUM

8 letters
DISLOYAL
PLAYMATE

9 letters
GUIDELINE
LIBERATOR

10 letters
ENTRAPMENT
OBITUARIST

11 letters
EQUILATERAL
GRAVEDIGGER

The Man She Married

With Lorna relishing her running and Rob glued to his armchair, could they narrow the distance between them?

By Valerie Bowes

I f you feel like that, why don't you just leave? You've made it plain enough you don't want to be here any more."

"You know what? I reckon I will. I'm sick of being the one who's always wrong."

"That's not fair!"

"Yes, it is, Lorna."

The anger boiling up inside her demanded an outlet.

"Well, you're not the man I married. Just look at yourself, Rob Cowling."

"Neither of us look the same as we did thirty-odd years ago. You can't expect it."

"You mean I don't measure up to the skinny beanpoles in your running club"

"I don't, but there's nothing to stop you taking a bit more care of yourself, is there?"

"Oh, I see!" he said with the air of someone who has experienced a light-bulb moment. "You mean I don't measure up to the skinny beanpoles at your running club? Well, for your information, I'm probably twice as old as they are. I'd like to see them when they're my age. Won't be such Greek gods then, will they?" He heaved himself to his feet. "But if that's what you want, you go ahead. I've had it."

She didn't really believe he'd walk out,

but he did. Tears slid down her face and dropped unheeded into a mug of cold tea.

He'd be back once he'd cooled down. It would give her time to pull herself together.

They never used to row like this, not even while the minefield of teenage hormones was exploding around them. If they were going to argue, you'd have thought it would have been when Erin was breaking her heart over a boy or Rob was furious about Josh coming in late.

She wasn't nagging, or comparing him unfavourably. She was merely concerned for his health. Wasn't she?

Since she'd joined this running club, she'd been more aware of the problems that getting older can bring. Of course she didn't expect to be able to run as fast as the twenty-somethings. But, as she and the other women her age agreed, they were out there doing it. Keeping fit and active, not sitting around, doing nothing and piling on the pounds. Like Rob.

She'd thought, when Erin started nursing and Josh took up an apprenticeship in electronics, that she and Rob would settle back to being a couple again, instead of being just Mum and Dad. They'd cruise ➤

through the years to a cosy retirement and grandparent duties. Together.

But it seemed that, without the glue of Erin and Josh to hold them together, something had gone missing.

"You don't have to do something because he does it – or vice versa. You don't have to be joined at the hip," said Lorna's friend Cathy. "It helps if you actually do something and he doesn't. He seems to have no interest in anything these days."

Lorna thought back to the games of darts they used to have with friends, of watching television feeling the warmth of Rob's body next to her on the sofa, of taking the kids swimming or walking in the countryside. They never did any of that any more.

"Anyway, he could do crochet and play cricket while I run and keep rabbits, but we need something in common as well. And that's the trouble, Cath. I don't think we have anything now."

Once he'd made his point, he'd be back. She just had to wait. She wouldn't mention any of this to Erin or Josh when they rang. But she would make a point of finding something she and Rob could both do.

It wouldn't be running, though. She'd had enough of his snide remarks about a woman her age trying to keep up with the younger ones.

"It's not a race, it's a run. Why don't you try it?" she'd coaxed.

He always laughed and shook his head.

"I'm not making a fool of myself."

"And I am, you mean?"

"Oh well, if you can't take a joke…"

So another row would begin.

When he didn't come back, she told herself she was glad. No more treading on eggshells, no more arguments and slamming doors. Life was more peaceful. She could get on with what she wanted to do without recriminations, silent or verbal.

So why did everything feel flat and empty? It was a good job she had her first Parkrun coming up in a few weeks' time. It gave her something to aim for.

Yes, she knew it wasn't a race. Yes, she did more than that distance on club runs. But she was still nervous. Jogging around with her friends was one thing; this would be the first time she'd be running with a crowd of people she didn't know and, whatever anyone said, it was still more like a race than anything she'd done so far.

But where's he gone, Mum?" She'd had to tell Erin at last that her dad had walked out.

"I don't know. He must have found somewhere to live, but he hasn't told me

where." She tried to keep the hurt from her voice for her daughter's sake. "He's taken some of his clothes and things, but not all.

"I don't know what's going on, love. I don't even know if he wants a divorce."

"Well, why don't you ask him?"

How often had Lorna said the same thing to Erin, when she and one of her friends fell out? But this was different.

"If he wants to talk to me, he knows where I am. I'm not the one who left."

Rob sat in the cafe, digging his heels in.

"Don't go on, Josh. I'm sick of the aggro."

"Bit drastic, though," said Josh, who could see how miserable his dad was. "It's been ages now. Couldn't you talk to her?"

Rob took a gulp of his coffee.

"Doing my own thing now," he said.

Josh shook his head. Honestly! Parents! What are they like? Which was much the same as Erin said when he phoned her.

"I think they'll have to sort it out themselves," she said reluctantly. "The more we stick our oars in, the more stubborn they'll get. We'll just have to stand by to pick up the pieces."

One minute there seemed to be oceans of time, the next Lorna was on her way to the Parkrun. She was going to meet Cathy there but there was no sign of her friend among the milling runners, all of whom looked far fitter and much faster than she could ever be.

Perhaps Rob had been right. Perhaps she was making a fool of herself. She looked round, willing Cathy to appear, dodging through the line-up at the start and burbling about roadworks.

But then she heard the shout of *Ready? Go!* and they were off. Lorna concentrated on the ground in front of her, on not slipping in the squidgy bits, on trying to catch up the person in front. Given it was a race only against yourself, it was surprising how much competitiveness crept in after she passed a girl she'd thought would be miles in front.

She came around the last bend and fairly flew over the last hundred yards to the finishing funnel. Clutching her token, she turned to see if anyone was coming in after her and was amazed at how many there were. Feeling very proud of herself, she went to get her barcode zapped to record her time. On the next run, she'd have something to aim at.

A message awaited her on her phone. *Car battery flat!* Cathy had texted. *Sorry!*

Typical Cathy! Always leaving her headlights on. But it would have been nice to have someone to share this moment with.

Even nicer if it had been Rob. The ➤

thought was so sudden it took her by surprise, and she had to hastily wipe her eyes.

A group of men came up to get their times registered. One of them, she thought wistfully through her tears, looked rather nice. Like Rob. Not the slouch he'd become, but more like a slightly chubbier version of the man she'd married.

Then his face reddened as he saw her.

She blinked the mistiness away.

"Rob?"

It couldn't be. Hadn't he said he wasn't going to make a fool of himself?

But he was coming slowly towards her.

"Beat me by a fair stretch," he said, grinning sheepishly.

Lorna smiled back.

"I've had more training."

"Well, you know…"

"Before we stopped being idiots and got back together, you mean?"

"Kind of." He grinned. "If you can't beat 'em…"

"You'll have to get a bit more training in before you do that!" she retorted.

"To be honest, I thought everyone'd laugh at me, but they've been so encouraging. Sort of made me see why you wanted to do something like this. Sorry, love. I shouldn't have teased you. It's hard work!"

And I should have seen what was bothering you, Lorna thought.

"Yes, but you did it," she said. "Neither of us are ready for pipe and slippers yet."

"If we ever are! Racing with zimmer frames might be a bit dodgy, but we'll find

"I was hoping to lose a bit of the old podge before I asked you to…"

Sweat lined his forehead, his top clung to a rounded belly and he still had a double chin. But there was something different about him that wasn't just the minimal loss of weight since she'd last seen him.

No. Not different. It was the old Rob, without the layer of defence he'd built up around the change in his life as the wheel turned, dependent kids became independent and no one seemed to need him any more.

"I didn't know you were doing it today," he said, on the defensive. "This is my first."

"Mine too," Lorna said.

He looked suddenly cheerful.

"I've been training with Chris from work. I was hoping to lose a bit of the old podge before I asked you to…"

"Before you asked me to do what?" Lorna said, her heart fluttering in a way that was nothing to do with running.

something to keep our minds active." He looked bashful. "Fancy coming for a coffee? Chris says they go to the Meets End caff afterwards."

It was almost like their first date, Lorna felt, with the same thrill of excitement as she'd had when Rob Cowling asked her out all those years ago. There'd have to be a few changes because life doesn't stand still, but she'd have to make them as well as him.

And it looked as if they'd always find something they could do together, after all. Ⓜ

ACT OF KINDNESS

I thought a long-planned running weekend in Derbyshire with my friends was off as I couldn't run with my arm in a sling, but they insisted I went and then they walked with me.

81
Calories per
biscuit

Nutmeg And Pistachio Biscotti

Ingredients (Makes 24)

- ◆ **50g whole blanched almonds**
- ◆ **175g plain flour**
- ◆ **40g polenta**
- ◆ **1½tsp baking powder**
- ◆ **115g caster sugar**
- ◆ **1tsp freshly grated nutmeg**
- ◆ **1 egg + 1 egg yolk, lightly beaten**
- ◆ **75g pistachio nuts**
- ◆ **2tsp grated lemon zest**

1 Preheat the oven to 170°C, Fan 150°C, Gas 3. Lightly grease 2 baking trays. Spread the almonds over one tray and roast for 7-10min, until light golden. Cool and coarsely chop.

2 Place the flour, polenta, baking powder, sugar and nutmeg in a bowl and mix together. Gradually mix in sufficient egg to form a soft dough.

3 Turn out onto a floured surface, sprinkle with the pistachio nuts, almonds and lemon zest and knead to distribute through the dough. Cut in two and roll each half into a sausage, about 5cm wide and 2.5cm thick.

4 Transfer to the remaining baking tray, spaced apart and bake for 25min, or until pale brown. Transfer to a wire rack and cook for 10min. Using a sharp serrated knife, cut diagonally into 2cm wide slices.

5 Return to the baking tray and cook for 12-15min, turning over after 8min. Transfer to a wire rack to cool. Store in an airtight container until ready to serve.

RECIPE AND FOOD STYLING: JENNIE SHAPTER PHOTOGRAPHY: JON WHITTAKER

Picking Up The Pieces

Just a jigsaw puzzle? Wrong! This was a serious competition with reputations on the line!

By Ella Ames

Small pieces of irregular shaped coloured cardboard covered the dining room tabletop.

"We have 1,000 pieces here," Molly announced looking at her husband.

"A walk in the park," Jed replied.

"Are we timing it?" Molly enquired.

"It would help… test our ability," he replied, spreading out the pieces.

Molly and Jed had become old hands at putting together jigsaw puzzles. They had been given one as a Christmas present, but having no interest in it at the time, they pushed it to the back of the cupboard under the stairs. Until a local power cut plunged them into darkness one evening. Unable to watch the TV they pulled out the jigsaw.

Over the next couple of hours they

As their enthusiasm grew, so did their collection, slowly increasing the number of pieces they assembled. They bought a range of jigsaw accessories, including boards, cases, frames, and roll-up mats. Molly and Jed's evenings had suddenly become more interesting. They no longer sat transfixed in separate chairs, sometimes in separate rooms, watching TV. Now they spent their evenings at the dining room table among an array of pieces, their skills improving with every puzzle. Having become skilled assemblers, they decided they should take their new hobby to another level and so they joined the Jigsters, a local jigsaw puzzle enthusiasts club.

"It's good for the brain," a fellow puzzler in his eighties announced. Professing it was puzzling that had kept his mind alert.

"The more puzzles you do, the more

Molly often commented that jigsaw puzzling had saved their marriage

slowly put the pieces together by torchlight. As they placed each piece into its correct place a sense of achievement surged through them, and they found themselves actually communicating with each other – something they had not done for several years. Molly would often comment that jigsaw puzzling had saved their marriage.

experience you gain, and I guess the better you become," another member had informed them. It was a friendly club with a mixture of young and old members who shared their techniques and tips with Molly and Jed. Who soon discovered there was more to puzzling than placing pieces together! Apparently, a rivalry existed between many of the clubs in particular the Jigsters and another local club known as the Puzzle-nerds.

This rivalry grew stronger each year when the Puzzle-nerds met up with the Jigsters in a friendly competition to test all the local clubs' abilities to complete a puzzle in the quickest time. According to Dave the Jigsters club leader, the Puzzle-nerds had previously been members of the Jigsters but their competitive nature had disrupted the ethos of the group, so they were asked to leave. Which they did reluctantly and formed their own club, led by Bill Jowett.

"They play dirty," Dave told Molly and Jed. "We believe they've stolen pieces from other team's puzzles to ensure they win. They're just down right saboteurs," he huffed. "But we haven't been able to prove it, as it's only when you get to the end of a puzzle you realise a piece is missing but there's no way of knowing when it went missing. But we have our suspicions. This time around we've asked the organisers to introduce some new rules – all the boxes to be sealed so they can't be tampered with beforehand. And not to allow members near other team tables, just in case someone uses sleight of hand to remove a piece," he tapped the side of his nose.

"But I think we stand a chance of winning this year," Dave continued, "I've discovered a new puzzler, just turned up at the club some weeks back. He's good, a keen eye for detail and very quick." All eyes turned to look at Dave with interest. "I'm going to include him as a member of the competition team. I wondered if," he turned to Jed, "you and Maddy would like to be in the team with myself as team leader?"

It delighted Jed and Maddy to be asked to join the competition group, they only hoped they were skilled enough to help them win. ➡

The day of the competition arrived, the village hall being the chosen venue. A faint smell of cabbage still lingered in the air from the pensioners luncheon club as they arranged tables around the room, each with four chairs. The puzzles, in plain boxes, each tightly sealed, lay in neat piles on a table carefully watched over by the competition organisers.

Dave looked at the hall clock as he wiped his sweaty hands down the sides of his trousers. He was feeling anxious. It was getting close to the starting time and his new expert had still not arrived.

"What happens if he doesn't turn up?" Molly asked, competition nerves setting in.

"We won't be allowed to play. Unless I can get a substitute here in the next couple of minutes."

Molly looked over at the Puzzle-nerds table. They sat looking confident and stared back at her determination flickering through their eyes.

Suddenly the hall's double doors opened with such a force it silenced the commotion in the hall. Everyone turned to the source of noise. The light from the corridor formed a long dark shadow over the figure standing in the doorway. He was 4ft 2 inches tall and 11 years of age.

"So, this must be Dave's secret weapon." Molly whispered as she nudged Jed in the side of his ribs.

The youngster stepped into the hall, arms held by his side. Only the sound of creaking floorboards disturbed the silence as he strode into the room. His shadow becoming smaller as he approached the table, the crowd parting to let him through.

As he approached the Jigsters table, Shelia, in charge of the competition, tapped on her microphone to test it was working.

"Welcome, puzzlers," her trill voice radiated out across the large hall. "Please make your way to your tables. We are about to begin."

A flurry of chatter ensued as last-minute tactics were discussed while others bent their heads together as if they were in a rugby scrum.

"Are you all ready? You know the rules – you have three hours in which to complete this identical 1,000-piece puzzle. The club to complete it in the fastest time is the winner of this magnificent trophy. She held it up high for everyone to see. Good luck!" She held her timer watch in front of her, silently counting down the seconds. "Go," she shouted.

The Jigsters began. As arranged Molly sorted the pieces into groups of colours, but she could not place them in their original orientation as she had no picture for guidance because it had been removed from all the puzzles to add to the challenge. Jed sorted pieces into a pile of inner and a pile of outer tabs, making it easier to connect pieces. The young lad, known as Jimmy the Kid because he was a love of cowboy films, began placing the corners and then the edges together – the best place to start – his fingers were small and nimble, and the pieces appeared to glide into place quickly.

When he had finished, he stood back to allow the others to place their pieces together, his hands twitching with eagerness to return to the task in hand.

"You have fifty minutes left," Shelia announced.

There was a gasp from one table. On other tables, furtive mumblings passed from member to member as if they were reviewing their plans and trying new tactics.

Shelia worked the floor, her watch held

tightly in her hand as she circumvented the tables like an ocean liner on a maiden voyage; she glided carefully around the tables, checking on everyone's progress. However, every now and again her foot would find a loose floorboard which made some tables wobble.

Table number four, the Puzzle-nerds glared at her as she approached them; they didn't like interruptions or their table wobbling they were intent on winning.

The Jigsters remained focused and now they just needed one piece to complete the puzzle. Jimmy scoured the table, but the piece was missing! They search the floor. They glanced over at their rivals. They appeared to be near completion, the gaps in their puzzle slowly getting smaller.

"It's them!" Molly announced, "They've stolen the last piece," she said looking across at their table, her jaw set tight.

"I don't see how," Jed replied.

"Neither do I," replied Dave, "We have all these security measures in place."

"Then it's got to be on the floor."

Jed looked at his watch. "And we were doing it in record time." The hall clock ticking appeared to grow louder while they frantically searched under the table.

The Puzzler-nerds looked up to see the Jigsters scrambling around on the floor. A smile fell across Bill Jowett's face.

"They're looking for a piece," one of the Puzzle-nerds announced. The rest of the team smiled at each other triumphantly.

It looked like they were going to win again this year.

This is terrible," Molly said, "to have come so far."

Jimmy the kid lifted his arms above him and rested them on the top of his head. He pressed down hard, as if doing so would engage his brain into solving the problem. Then he realised something was fluttering

past his face. It twirled its way down to the ground and landed softly at his foot.

"Aha!" shouted Molly, "It's the missing piece! It must have got stuck in the cuff of your jumper." She picked it up and placed in its space with a loud gratifying snap.

"We've won!" they all shouted in unison as Shelia stopped her watch, announcing that the Jigsters had completed the puzzle in 171 minutes.

With the minimum of fuss, they pushed Jimmy the Kid towards the stage. Everyone had agreed he should collect the trophy, having been their secret weapon.

The Puzzle-nerds accepted their defeat surprisingly well, considering they always liked to win. But this was probably because it was rumoured they had bigger fish to fry. They had the world puzzle championships in Spain in their sights. Spain was all about prestige and big prize money.

At the end of the evening, everyone made their way home. The Jigsters, carrying their trophy world cup style above their heads, made their way to the pub to celebrate. Leaving behind the puzzle-nerds and a few stragglers in the hall.

Bill Jowett strode over to Jimmy, sitting at a table waiting for his mother to pick him up. Bill leaned in and whispered in Jimmy's ear, "All you had to do was keep that piece up your sleeve, but you had to raise your arms, didn't you? You ruined it. So, if you're thinking you're coming to Spain with us son, you can think again."

"Sorry, Dad," Jimmy replied. **MW**

. . . .

ACT OF KINDNESS

I try to do an act of kindness every day. A simple one to do is to offer your place in the supermarket queue to someone who only has a few items in their basket.

Over The Line

Had Ginny gone too far when she finally had the chance for revenge? And what would the repercussions be?

By Lin Silver

Ginny and her best pals Tasha and Katie loved going to the sports ground after school.

Not that there was anything there – basically it was just a large open field with a pavilion at one end and big old trees all round the edge.

However it had two big advantages – firstly, it was just up the road from all three of their homes so no one objected to them going off there alone; and secondly, it was also the place where Josh and his friends played football every night.

"I'll get Josh tonight," Ginny vowed through clenched teeth, pulling a ferocious face. "Did you see what he did when him and Craig were sat behind me in Double English? He tied my plaits together!"

"Oh, we'll teach him," vowed Tasha. "He told me I looked like a radish when I wore that red dress for choir practice!"

"He's so horrible," added Ginny. "He thinks he's the king of the world or something, just because he can kick a ball around. And that stupid Trina Shaw in Miss Duncan's class really likes him…"

The small group of boys were already engrossed in their game of football when the girls arrived .

"Yah! Pickle! Canary! What d'you look like, in that stupid kit?"

The girls sneered and called out, trying to put them off their shots by jumping about and waving wildly.

"Clear off, rag-bags!" came the retort from Johnson, who thought he was *it*.

"You clear off. This is our park. We don't want your lot here!" said Ginny.

Josh came running up, looking angry, but she stood her ground.

"You tied my hair up. Why d'you do that? I don't touch your filthy barnet!"

"Yeah, your stupid pigtail things were dabbing all over my work book," said Josh, scathingly.

"Yeah, doesn't even know a plait from a pigtail!" Ginny sneered, and the girls laughed.

"I know when something needs cutting off!" growled Josh. But his mates were calling him and he turned away. "I'm here to play, not waste my time on ugly idiots like you!" he muttered.

"Play? You couldn't score a goal if the ball was as big as the net!" Ginny sneered.

The boys ran back to the pitch and Ginny and her mates stood around watching, hoping for an opportunity to put them off. Suddenly, Neil missed the ball and it came hurtling at top speed towards the three girls.

Kate caught it, and before Neil could stop her, Ginny had snatched it and hurled it right over the fence and into the road that ran alongside.

"What did y'do that for, you toxic little germ?" Neil yelled.

Josh was first on the scene, keen to wipe the smug smile off Ginny's face. But she got her words in first. ➜

"That's your match ruined, same as my hair was this morning. Let's call it quits, shall we?"

"Not likely," muttered Josh, fuming. "I'll get you, Ginny Lockhart. Just you wait."

"Ooh, I'm so scared!" Ginny said, faking sheer terror, as Tasha and Kate laughed and fell about.

"It's Trina Shaw who'll get you, Joshua Heath," said Tasha, once she'd recovered a bit. "She loves you to death, didn't you know? She wants to marry you, an' she's going to get you…"

"Shut up, you don't know what you're on about," Josh muttered, going bright red and looking around to see if any of his mates had heard. Fortunately they were more preoccupied with retrieving their ball. Being teased about a girl was the ultimate insult when you were nine.

qualifications and landed a plum job with a prestigious advertising agency. Over five years, she worked her way up to become chief co-ordinator of the photoshoots to promote their clients' products.

"It's the big sports campaign next week," said her boss, Josie, one morning. "You'll be wanted for the man-spray campaign. They're filming at the stadium and apparently they've got some big sporting names lined up."

Ginny smiled.

"OK," she said. Sport wasn't really her thing, but doing a good job was.

At the start of the following week she turned up promptly at the massive football ground, home of many big-name games, and fought her way through

"It's Trina Shaw who'll get you, Joshua Heath. She loves you to death…"

A few years passed, and Ginny and co began to stop disliking boys so much. In fact, it was going the opposite way – they were actually starting to like them.

Josh and his footballing friends didn't go to the sports ground any more – when they'd moved up to secondary schools, he'd gone to the Academy High, that had its own ground for sports. Ginny, Tasha and Kate went to the brand new comprehensive and soon Josh and his childish pranks were completely forgotten.

Although Kate did report seeing him once in town looking round a sports shop and that he was covered in spots…

Time moved on, as time always does. Ginny left school with an impressive list of

a hectic mass of excited girls waving posters, scarves and autograph books, chanting, "Josh! Josh! We love Josh! Josh is a winner, Josh is gonna score! Josh, Josh, Josh! We want more!"

Ginny smiled and shook her head. Daft fans! Who was this guy, anyway? She didn't follow footie, no one in her family was keen, either – so she supposed he was just someone who made the headlines in the sporting pages. And presumably he was a bit of a dish.

The representative from the company of the product they were to be advertising appeared, a pleasant Japanese guy in smart casual clothes.

"Hi. You must be Ginny Lockhart. Ken

Buko." He smiled and they shook hands. "Now, we've managed to snare one of the best role models for our body spray range. It was touch and go but we outbid our rival contenders. You must know, from the fan club gathered outside – City striker Josh Heath?"

For a second, Ginny thought she must have misheard. Josh Heath? But surely – wasn't that – it couldn't be – Oh, Lord!

"I'll show you around," said Ken, unaware of her confusion. "We want to film outside, on the pitch, of course. We want him scoring a goal with the caption 'Always a Winner'. Then you come into it, Ginny – synchronise the glamorous models we've booked homing in on him as they catch the scent of his luxe body spray. How does that sound?"

"Good," Ginny murmured, managing to keep her cool while inside she was all sixes and sevens. Still trying hopelessly to convince herself *it couldn't be,* she followed Ken to the goal area.

"Ah, here is the man of the moment now!" her host said, smiling widely. "Come for a few rehearsals…"

Ginny swallowed the boulder that had somehow formed in her throat. He wasn't a mucky little brat now. He certainly wasn't covered with acne! He was a very attractive man. And it was definitely him. No wonder there was such a throng of admirers clustered outside, desperate for a glimpse. He was gorgeous!

More to the point, he'd seen her. And he was staring back, as astonished as she.

"Excuse, folks, is something wrong?" Ken asked nervously, sensing the tension immediately. Well, it was so thick you'd need a chainsaw to cut it.

Josh spoke first, thankfully. Ginny felt sure she'd been rendered speechless.

"No, everything's wowzer," he grinned, dropping the ball he was holding and bouncing it up and down a few times in readiness. "As a matter of fact, Ken, Ginny and I go way back…"

He remembered her name! What else did he remember? Was he about to open up and ruin her credibility?

"Oh, better and better," said the promotions man, obviously pleased and relieved, assuming they were old friends.

"Hey, Ginny," Josh said, lasering her with a direct gaze from his deep blue eyes, "It's good to see you again – really good."

The atmosphere had changed in an instant and Ginny relaxed as a different kind of tension flowed through her veins. They were not cantankerous little kids now. What they'd said and done almost twenty years ago was of another age. But… There was no mistaking the look of latent humour on Josh's face as he took aim and fired…

The ball flew past her head at goodness knows how many miles an hour and straight into the back of the net. But far from dwelling on her narrow escape from decapitation, Ginny was spurred into immediate action when she saw the opportunity that had arisen. Without hesitation, she snatched up the ball ➡

and hurled it high and wide over the pitch and way up into the back row of spectators' seating.

"Why, you little…" Josh was trying not to laugh as he ran towards her, trying to look menacing just as he'd tried to back in the days of the sports ground. "When I get hold of you, I'll…"

Ginny screamed with laughter, kicked off her shoes and began running – slowly – away from him.

"Well, you can't tie my plaits up, because my hair's short now!"

"Don't worry, I'll think of something else," Josh replied, gaining on her. "Like – suggesting we go for a drink and a chat once this filming malarkey's out the way?"

He was close now, and the next second they both came to a standstill.

"Believe it or not, it's good to see you

She felt empowered, and loving it.

"White," said Josh, firmly.

"Both, then," said Ginny. "I suspect we'll be at that table for a long time."

As this went on, poor Ken Buko was standing with his mouth open. Josh and Ginny realised at the same moment and turned to him.

"Sorry, we're just reliving old times," said Josh. "But we're good to go with the ad, now, Ken, whenever you're ready."

With obvious relief, Ken went to rally his troops. Josh winked at Ginny.

"I'll see you after we're done," he said.

"I'll be waiting in the wings," Ginny grinned. She turned to go, then felt his hand gentle but firm on her shoulder.

"Oh – not quite yet," he said sternly. "There's still something you need to do first, isn't there?"

Ginny screamed with laughter and began running – slowly – away from him

again," he said, a certain kind of awareness evident in his eyes. "Wow, you've changed! But I'd love an update – on everything since those scatty days we had as kids…"

"I'd love to tell all," Ginny murmured, "and hear all, about your rise to footie stardom!"

Josh looked sheepish.

"Well, I'm hardly Premier League," he said with a modest shrug.

"Yet," Ginny said, with emphasis. "Did you ever go out with Trina Shaw, by the way?" The smile threatened to crack her jaw as she waited for his reply.

"Who?" He looked blank.

Obviously not, then.

"Oh, don't worry – we can go over everything in minute detail once we're sitting down somewhere with a bottle of red between us," she chuckled.

What would that be? Kiss him, or – "What?"

"Climb all the way up to the back row of the stadium and find that ball you so thoughtfully hurled up there," Josh said.

Ginny tried hard to fake annoyance as she tramped off, over the pitch and up into the seating.

"I'll get you, Josh Heath," she mumbled to herself.

But somehow, those words held a very different significance now… **MW**

✦ *Cats & Dogs* in 2001 starred a host of big name voices in an animated action comedy with some very hit-and-miss jokes!

✦ The new millennium began with an Ice Age... yes it did – the movie *Ice Age* in 2002 brought mammoth frozen family fun aplenty!

✦ Frozen frolics were on offer in 2006 with the hugely popular movie, *Happy Feet*. Penguins find a mate with a song, but Muble can't sing... Happily he has some killer dance moves.

✦ The 1993 classic *Free Willy* saw the fostered and troubled Jesse bond with lonely captive Orca Willy. And who didn't cheer when he finally leads Willy to freedom?

FANCY THAT!

Fascinating facts on **Animal Movies!**

✦ 2020 brought not just lockdown, but *The Call Of The Wild*, starring a grizzly older Harrison Ford in a reasonable adaptation of a classic story.

✦ The 1993 hit *Turner & Hooch* was a rather silly cops and robbers movie, starring a slobbering Hooch and a youthful Tom Hanks.

✦ *Lady And The Tramp* in 1955 – yes, it really was as far back as that! – was the movie that ensured we would never look at a plate of spaghetti the same way again.

The 1943 classic, *Lassie Come Home*, was set in Britain during the Depression and starred an 11-year-old Elizabeth Taylor

✦ In 2018, Beatrix Potter's beloved tale got the modern-day treatment in the live-action movie with the lead character's name, *Peter Rabbit*.

✦ A rat in a restaurant? Eek! But we all loved the antics of a rat named Remy who just happened to be a culinary wizard, in *Ratatouille* in 2007.

Penny For The Guy

A return to old traditions might be just what's needed to help Bea's family through a difficult time

By Julia Douglas

It's not fair!" Maisie's eyebrows knitted behind her fashionable glasses. "Just because Dad's lost his job he says we can't go to the firework display."

Bea regarded the smartly-dressed eleven-year-old with sympathy. Her son-in-law had always worked hard. It wasn't his fault the firm he worked for had closed down, making hundreds redundant.

"I expect money's a bit tight at the moment," Bea said gently. It was fortunate that her daughter had a job, although she doubted one income went far these days. Her granddaughters had come to expect every luxury their friends had. She hoped things weren't going to change too drastically for them.

Maisie's nine-year-old sister, Chloe, looked up from her smartphone just long enough to plead, "Can't you take us to the fireworks, Gran? They're having a laser show and everything."

"When I was your age," Bea smiled, "my friend and I put on our own firework display for all our schoolmates."

"Wow! Were you really rich?" Maisie asked in wonder.

"Far from it," Bea chuckled.

Looking back, she'd had nothing – certainly compared to her granddaughters. But neither had she wanted for anything.

Oh, no, not again!" Bea's mum cursed the change in the wind that brought a thick cloud of smoke and cinders sweeping down the railway embankment into her back garden, enveloping her freshly hung washing.

Bea, a skinny, blonde eleven-year-old, took advantage of her mother's distraction to slip out of the back gate with her best friend, Jackie.

"I managed to get some old trousers and a jumper off my mum." Jackie's brown hair shone in the chilly Saturday morning sun. "They were my brother's when he was little."

"We only need a pram, then," said Bea. "Let's try the dump."

Weaving through narrow alleys between backyards where dogs barked, children shrieked and adults shouted, they emerged on a street facing a row of condemned terraced houses.

Boards had been pulled from several glassless windows and although the houses were fenced off, a hole had long ago been torn in the wood and wire barrier.

Bea's stomach tensed nervously as the girls ducked through a dank arched tunnel in the middle of the terrace.

She knew the houses were home to tramps and all sorts of dangers. Her parents had told her many times to never enter them. But, she reasoned, she wouldn't be going into the houses, would she?

They emerged from the passage into a sunny area that would once have been occupied by back gardens and outside toilets but which was now a wide, shallow bomb crater, overgrown with brambles and used as a rubbish tip by residents of the surrounding streets.

"Careful," Jackie warned unnecessarily as they picked their way down a winding path, rubble slipping beneath their feet.

Bea looked back at the terrace they'd passed through. From the street, the houses had looked fairly intact, but from this side the bomb damage was far more evident. Whole sections of wall had been ripped away revealing battered rooms stacked above each other.

It was like looking into a weather-damaged doll's house. Blackened wallpaper flapped beneath collapsed rafters. Rubble-covered beds and ancient brown wardrobes still stood on the upper floors.

"Imagine living here during the war," Bea mused.

Her mum had told her stories about air raid sirens and shelters, but to Bea they were tales from another time. They felt no more real to her than fairytales of princesses and dragons, even though the evidence of conflict was all around her.

"Lucky you weren't sitting there." Jackie pointed to half a lavatory pan, gleaming among a tangle of dry brown bramble stems, and they both laughed.

"Now, that's what we're looking for." Bea spied the white tyre of a pram wheel poking from another skeletal bush. "Help me get it out."

"What a beauty," Jackie declared.

The pram was dented and covered in rust. Its canopy was just a few scraps of navy blue cloth hanging from a wire frame, but it rolled freely on its four wheels.

"I'll ride, you push!" Bea declared when they got back to the street. The springs sagged with a loud squeak as she jumped into the pram, her dirty knees hooked over the front.

"Why have I got to push?" Jackie protested.

"You can have a turn later."

"Well, if you insist," Jackie smirked. "Fine – let's see how fast you want to go, then!"

"Slow down, slow down! Help!" Bea screamed giddily as her pal charged down the street, pushing the pram as fast as her legs would carry her.

"Look out!" Bea yelled as a shiny black Ford Popular turned into the end of the road, heading straight for them. ➤

Desperately Jackie steered the pram into the kerb and they cartwheeled onto the pavement as the rickety contraption overturned. Both girls were as bruised and grazed as each other, but they were laughing too much to feel it.

A lifetime later, Bea stood under the railway bridge that crossed the high street, wrapped up in coat, scarf, hat and gloves in the windy November dusk.

Red buses ploughed past with a rumble that echoed off the bridge's blackened brick walls. Pigeons cooed and flapped among the nets and girders above her head.

"Penny for the guy!" Maisie and Chloe called as they stood in matching pink hooded coats beside the station's entrance. In a pushchair sat a child-size figure made from old clothes stuffed with newspaper. His grinning face was painted onto a piece of cardboard beneath grey hair made from the head of a mop.

The pushchair hadn't come from the dump, but from the back of Bea's shed, along with the handle-less mop. The clothes were her son's, retrieved from a cardboard box on a dusty expedition into the darkest recesses of her loft.

Her children laughed at her for never throwing anything away, but she'd grown

the way their gran had.

The commuters spilling from the station looked happy to reward the girls' entrepreneurialism with shiny fifty pences and pounds, and her rosy-cheeked grandchildren looked more alive than they ever did when they were glued to their social media accounts.

"You remind me of me when I was your age," a woman with greying brown hair told them. "I used to stand on this very spot with my friend –"

The woman glanced up and her mouth fell open.

"Bea!" She grinned.

"Jackie!" Bea hugged her tightly. "What are you doing here?"

"Ron and I are moving back to town to be nearer the kids. I've just been round to your place to surprise you, but you weren't there, obviously."

"Where are you moving to?" Bea asked, intrigued

"We're buying one of those new retirement places where the old dump used to be. Just around the corner from you. It'll be just like the old days!"

G uy watched the endless lights of suburbia as the electric train trundled homeward. He thought the interview had gone pretty well. But then, he

In a pushchair sat a child-sized figure, with grey hair made from a mop

up knowing that anything might come in handy one day.

Stamping her feet to keep warm, Bea stood a discreet distance from her granddaughters. Their mum would have kittens if she let them stand there alone, the way she and Jackie used to, but Maisie and Chloe wanted to feel as if they were raising the money all by themselves,

remembered with a sigh, he'd thought the same about the one he had last week.

That one had been his dream job and he'd felt certain he was the right man for the post. They'd told him they'd be in touch in a couple of days, and he'd felt sure it was in the bag.

So far, though, he'd heard nothing. He wondered if his hopes would be dashed with yet another letter in the mail saying there had been a lot of applicants and that sadly he hadn't been successful.

By the time the train pulled into his station, he was feeling dejected.

A distant fizz turned his head. From the elevated railway platform he saw a rocket streak into the sky on the far side of town.

The firework fizzled out disappointingly, a bit like his hopes of finding work.

As he left the station, his phone beeped and he quickly fumbled it from his pocket. Could it be the company he'd just left, telling him the job was his?

He deflated as he found a text from his wife, Cathy, reminding him to collect Maisie and Chloe from her mum's.

He dreaded meeting his mother-in-law's eye when she asked the inevitable

daughter took his hand and dragged him eagerly down the hall into the kitchen.

"Sausage sandwich, love?" Bea handed him a plate that smelled delicious.

"Bea, you needn't have…" Guy began, although he was touched.

"Not me," Bea corrected. "The girls earned the money to pay for everything – even the sausages."

His head spinning, Guy was led through the back door. Half a dozen children were excitedly eating hot, greasy sandwiches on the patio. With them were a couple of parents he recognised from the school gates.

In the shadows at the bottom of the garden a greying woman he didn't recognise was guiding Maisie as she lit a firework at arm's length.

Chloe opened the door. "Daddy! Brilliant. You're just in time for the display"

question about his job hunt.

It wasn't as if he wasn't trying. He was beginning to wonder if the interviewers could see his desperation – and that it marked him down as a loser no one would ever employ again.

Trudging down a street of Victorian terraced houses, Guy wondered if he should relent and take the girls to that firework display – they all needed something to cheer them up. But he knew he had to save the money for their Christmas presents.

At his mum-in-law's, he was surprised to find a balloon tied to the gate and a cardboard arrow that bore the message, *Fireworks – this way.*

Chloe opened the door.

"Daddy!" Her blue eyes shone excitedly. "Brilliant. You're just in time for the display."

"What's all this?" Guy asked as his

"Now let's go and stand well back with the others," Jackie was saying.

Guy's phone beeped and he fished it out of his pocket.

"I don't believe it." He stared at the text in astonishment.

"Good news?" asked Bea at his side.

"That job I was telling you about last week – it's mine!"

A cheer went up from kids and adults alike as a corner shop Roman candle lit up the garden with a fountain of golden sparks that was more beautiful than any firework display Guy had ever seen. 🄼🅆

Sparks And Sparklers!

The village Bonfire Night celebration was hotting up in more ways than one for newcomer Evie…

By Jan Snook

x

Evie stared at the computer screen, taking in the columns of figures before her. Although she'd been thrilled to be offered the job, even she was surprised at just how absorbing the research that she was engaged in was.

It was Monday morning, the second week into her new job, and she was pleased at how at home she already felt. At work, at least, she amended. Home was quite another matter.

All around her people were taking off their coats, making coffee and talking about their respective weekends, before settling down to work.

"What about you, Evie?" her immediate boss Joanna asked kindly. "Did you do anything special?"

"Well, no." Evie hesitated. She could hardly say that having moved three hundred miles to take the job, she now found herself in a town where she didn't know a soul other than her work colleagues, and so had sat around in her poky (but eye-wateringly expensive) little flat, making important decisions like where the biscuit tin should live. Homesickness was a new sensation for her, and she didn't like it.

"I had a few things to do in the flat – and I don't really know many people here yet," she added, with what she hoped was a convincing smile.

She must have failed, because Joanna's face fell.

"Of course you don't. I'm sorry, I should have thought." Then her face brightened. "But next weekend it's our village Bonfire Night. It's on the Saturday, not the night itself, but it should be fun. Why don't you come? I live just by the village green, so a few of us are meeting at my house beforehand – they're mostly married couples with children, but there are a few younger ones coming too. I hope you've got some wellies!"

"I live just by the village green and a few of us are meeting at my house"

She gave Evie times and directions and repeated that it would be fun.

Evie found herself looking forward to it more than she expected to, considering that the last people she wanted to meet at the moment were smug young marrieds with children. She had thought not long ago that she would be joining them ➡

y

z

herself soon. She and Stephen, that was. But then, out of the blue – after setting a date and making plans, though thankfully before sending out invitations – Stephen had announced that they were too young, and needed a cooling-off period. And after six whole weeks of cooling off, he had announced his engagement to someone else. Which had sent Evie scuttling south to a new job and a new life.

A life, as it happened, without Wellington boots. So first thing on Saturday she went out and bought some.

Saturday evening was crisp, cold and starry. Evie wrapped up warmly and drove tentatively out of town, through the unfamiliar lanes to the village where Joanna lived.

Joanna's husband Paul opened the door and led her into an already crowded room. There were a number of excited

"My brother's around somewhere," Joanna said, as if reading her mind. "He's a doctor at the Royal, only just qualified. He got a lift here with a couple of friends. His name's Tom. Tall. Horn-rimmed specs," she said helpfully. "Just got to turn the oven down, then we'll go. You are coming back for a spot of supper afterwards, aren't you? Did I say?"

Evie fixed a smile on her face and tried to blend in with the crowd, who were soon traipsing out of the house, suitably attired, and armed with torches, to cross to the village green. She couldn't see anyone who might be Joanna's brother – or indeed his friends.

The green was dominated by a vast bonfire – just being lit – and a lumpy guy sitting on the very top. All around were stalls selling hot chocolate, burgers, sausages and roasted chestnuts. From a First Aid tent a voice was booming out

The sight of so many families enjoying being together made her heart ache

children zooming around, and adults who looked up to say hello when she was introduced, but were otherwise engrossed in searching for missing mittens or stray boots. The smell of potatoes baking was coming from the kitchen, and Joanna appeared in an apron to greet her.

"We'll be off in a minute," she said, looking at her watch. "It's never a very prompt start, but the children are dying to get going as you see!"

Evie looked around to see if she could spot anyone who looked remotely unattached, but failed.

over the loud speaker system asking for the parents of four-year-old Luke to come and collect him. Further on, a brass band was playing under a gazebo. There was an air of suppressed excitement as groups of people huddled together, waiting for the fireworks to begin.

In the increasing light (and heat) of the bonfire, shadowy figures could be seen moving among the firework stands, ready to light the blue touch papers. Children were sitting on their fathers' shoulders and

a hush settled over the green as the first whoosh of a rocket split the sky with a thousand golden stars, rapidly followed by fizzing Catherine wheels, popping firecrackers, Roman candles bursting into a torrent of sparks and an army of rockets. Every head was tipped back, and the air was full of the synchronised oohs and aahs of the crowd.

It was hard not to enjoy it, Evie thought, and she knew she would have been miserable if she'd stayed at home, hearing the bangs and splutters of half-glimpsed fireworks through her windows. She was glad she'd come out, but the sight of so many happy families enjoying being together made her heart ache. She shook herself. Self-pity was despicable.

After at least twenty minutes of the sky being rent with explosions of colour, a voice came over the loudspeakers informing the crowd that there would be a ten-minute interval before the grand finale of spectacular set pieces, and that they should go and buy all the goodies on sale, as the profits would go towards making next year's display even bigger and better.

Evie breathed in wafts of smoky bonfire and the gunpowder smell of spent fireworks as clouds of ash rained down on the spectators.

A couple of children were dancing up and down at her feet, and she recognised them as Joanna's little girls, who were six and eight. Joanna, though, was nowhere in sight.

"Are you having a lovely time?" Evie asked the smaller child brightly.

At her words, the nearest couple looked around. And there were the horn rimmed glasses she'd been looking for at last.

Attached to a tall good-looking man who would normally have caught her attention at once. How had Evie not noticed him before?

The answer, probably, was because he was so obviously with someone. A woman was clinging to Tom's arm: Evie had noticed her earlier, jumping in exaggerated fright at every little bang.

"I hope my nieces aren't annoying you," Tom said, struggling to free his hand, and proffering it. "I'm Joanna's brother, Tom…"

"And I'm Annabelle," the girl said firmly, stepping between them and anchoring his arm to her side again as quickly as she could.

Annabelle was smiling artificially at her, and with an effort Evie smiled back.

"I was about to go and get us some hot chocolate," Tom said. "Can I get you some as well?"

Evie hesitated for a second, but Annabelle had already jumped in.

"I'll come with you to help you carry them," she said decisively to Tom. "I expect we'll be able to find… Edie…?"

"Evie," Tom corrected her. An irritated frown flickered across Annabelle's face.

"Evie, then," she said, rolling her ➜

eyes. "I hope we'll be able to find Evie again in this crowd. Though of course it's very dark. Not easy to see."

Tom glanced down at Annabelle's feet.

"It's very muddy over by the hot chocolate stand and, as you just said, you're not in the right footwear for it."

It was true, Evie now saw. Annabelle was wearing flimsy flat shoes that were already caked in mud and grass. She didn't even seem to be wearing socks. She must be freezing.

"I'll be fine," Annabelle said, "you can't carry three. And what about the children, don't they want any?"

"I tell you what," Tom said amiably, "why don't you stay and look after Chloe and Imogen, and Evie and I can go and get the drinks? Evie's wearing wellies."

Evie nearly laughed at the expression of horror on Annabelle's face.

"It's fine," Evie said. "I can keep an eye on the children, don't worry. And thanks, but I won't have anything to drink."

continued miserably, "I wanted to introduce you to him. He arrived with Gavin and his girlfriend but now I can only find Gavin."

"Annabelle's not my girlfriend," Gavin said crossly. "She just tagged along. She's impossible to get rid of. Except," he amended, "now she's flounced off because I said she was stupid not to come in wellies. She's a nightmare, she really is."

But Evie hardly heard. Her heart had skipped a beat. Or quite a few beats.

Joanna was now talking to the girls.

"… so I'll light them and you must hold on to them very tightly and not wave them near anyone, remember?"

A minute later the sparklers were lit, and the children were making patterns and writing their names in the cold night air.

One sparkler followed another until the voice over the loudspeaker asked the villagers to join him in a countdown till the fireworks began again.

"What's happened?" Tom shoved the hot chocolates at a protesting Annabelle

Tom met her eyes over Annabelle's head, his forehead puckered.

"Well, if you're sure," he said over his shoulder as Annabelle positively dragged him away, her shoes squelching audibly.

Joanna appeared, along with another man whom she introduced as Gavin.

"I'm sorry," Joanna said, "I had no idea that you'd been abandoned to look after my children. Where's Tom?" But before Evie could answer, Joanna

"Ten! Nine! Eight…" the crowd was roaring, "Seven! Six! Five! Four…"

All the faces were tilted skywards again, waiting for the whoosh of the first firework. "Three! Two! …"

The final "One!" almost drowned Imogen's squeal as she dropped her hot sparkler.

"Help!" Evie shouted at the same time, but the adults were checking that Imogen hadn't burned herself, and only Tom, who was returning laden with drinks, heard her.

"What's happened?" he asked, hurtling towards her and shoving the hot chocolates at a protesting Annabelle.

"The sparkler… she dropped it down my welly," Evie said, struggling to pull off her boot and trying hard not to cry.

The group's attention switched abruptly from Imogen to Evie. Gavin switched on his torch and pulled her boot off while Tom supported her. Without a word Joanna drew her keys out of her pocket and made to return to the house, but Tom stopped her.

"Put the keys in my pocket. My bag's at your house."

And without another word he scooped Evie up and began to run.

"For heaven's sake, it's only a sparkler…" Annabelle could be heard saying petulantly to anyone who would listen, but Tom and Evie were soon safely out of earshot.

"Please, put me down – you don't have to carry me," Evie protested. "I'm sure I can walk."

"You certainly can't walk in this mud without your boot on," Tom said reasonably. "I can't see the burn properly in this light, and also we don't want it to get infected."

They had in any case arrived at Joanna's house, and Tom put Evie gently down on the front step while he unlocked the door. Behind them the sky was being lit up once again by fireworks, as he led Evie – wincing at every step – to the nearest chair.

"My doctor's bag's in the car. Don't move."

Evie smiled weakly. It seemed he wasn't going anywhere.

Tom returned, bag in hand, and started to remove Evie's sock very carefully. There was a nasty burn right through the sock, and he winced in sympathy as Evie drew in her breath sharply.

"The trouble with this is that the sparkler had nowhere to go once it was inside your boot," he said as he cleaned the area, put a jelly-like substance over the affected area and covered it with a dressing. "Just as well you'd got really thick socks on."

He talked as he worked, and seemed to know a surprising amount about her – thanks to Joanna presumably.

Tom had just got around to saying that perhaps (as she worked so close to the hospital) they could meet up for lunch one day, when the door opened and throngs of Joanna's guests poured into the hall, chattering happily while they stripped off hats, coats, scarves and gloves. Evie was soon surrounded by concerned well-wishers, including Gavin, who said sorrowfully that he'd brought her boot back with him, but that it was, he ➔

thought, burned beyond repair.

"Pity," he said, "it looked almost new."

Evie looked around, and Gavin, guessing her motives, laughed.

"If you're looking for Annabelle, I'm afraid she's gone off in a huff. You both missed quite a scene, actually. Your boot's wrecked, and so's my jacket! Covered in hot chocolate that the dear lady threw at me. She had quite a supply."

Evie gasped in horror, but Tom hooted with laughter.

"Serves you right for landing me with her," he said. Then he added thoughtfully, "Of course if you hadn't, poor Evie wouldn't have ended up watching over Imogen and I might not have had the chance to get to know her – though I'll be having a few words with my niece about health and safety."

Gradually the guests wandered into the kitchen to help themselves to jacket potatoes and sausages, and Evie found herself alone once more with Tom. He really was remarkably good-looking, she thought. And very tall.

The rest of the evening passed all too quickly, burn or no burn, and Evie hoped that Tom hadn't just been being polite about meeting for lunch in the week – though he hadn't mentioned it again.

"I'd better take you home, I think," he said tentatively as guests began to leave. "I came in Gavin's car, so I could drive you home in your car, if that's OK. I don't think you'd better do any driving with that foot tonight."

Evie's heart leapt. She'd be with him for a little while longer.

It wasn't until he'd delivered her to her own front door that the subject of seeing her again came up.

"About lunch," he said, and her heart – which had been behaving like a yo-yo ever since she laid eyes on him – plummeted as his brow furrowed. "The trouble with being a doctor is that I'm never sure what I'm doing until the last minute, and I wouldn't want to let you down, so perhaps we'd better leave a mid-week lunch for the moment. I never have very long to eat anyway."

So he was letting her down gently, at least. "But I'm off duty tomorrow, and some of the pubs round here do a very good Sunday lunch – are you busy?" He smiled a slow and delectable smile. "And maybe we should go and buy you some new wellies, so that we could go for a walk afterwards. What do you think?"

Then the business-like doctor took over once more. "Oh, and painkillers for you, young lady, before you go to bed."

And although he administered some, Evie privately thought that happiness was the best painkiller ever. Ⓜ

ACT OF KINDNESS

When my mother lived in Chile many years ago (before Talking Books in English were obtainable there), she read and recorded more than twenty novels for a blind friend – some of them very dry reading indeed!

Brain Boosters SOLUTIONS

CODEWORD FROM PAGE 35
PHRASE: STOCK AITKEN WATERMAN

KRISS KROSS FROM PAGE 133

MISSING LINK FROM PAGE 53
ACROSS: 1 Body 3 Powered 8 White
9 Along 10 Lid 12 Ditch 14 Cause
16 Cream 20 Owner 22 Hoe 24 Court
25 Media 27 Liberal 28 Army
DOWN: 1 Battle 2 Dew 3 Pretty
4 Weather 5 Root 6 Digger 7 Bird
11 Draw 13 Path 15 Shooter
17 Parcel 18 Animal 19 Beauty
21 Rude 23 Dumb 26 Air
SHADED WORD: BROLLY

MISSING LINK FROM PAGE 101
ACROSS: 1 Straw 4 Coast 7 King
8 Function 9 Dancer 11 Peak
12 Path 14 Tail 17 Bath 18 Butter
19 Mistress 21 Flag 22 Yards
23 Canal
DOWN: 1 Spiral 2 Rag 3 Wafer
4 Concert 5 Ant 6 Trojan 10 Coach
11 Print 13 Holders 15 Vanity
16 Retail 18 Basic 20 Tar 21 Fan
SHADED WORD: SAFARI

SUDOKU 1 FROM PAGE 119

3	4	5	6	1	8	7	2	9
8	7	6	4	2	9	1	5	3
1	9	2	3	7	5	6	8	4
5	1	4	7	8	3	9	6	2
7	2	8	9	6	4	3	1	5
6	3	9	1	5	2	4	7	8
2	6	3	8	4	7	5	9	1
9	5	7	2	3	1	8	4	6
4	8	1	5	9	6	2	3	7

SUDOKU 2 FROM PAGE 119

7	1	8	3	2	6	4	5	9
2	6	9	7	5	4	8	1	3
5	4	3	1	8	9	6	7	2
9	3	2	4	7	1	5	6	8
4	7	5	8	6	3	9	2	1
1	8	6	2	9	5	3	4	7
6	5	1	9	3	7	2	8	4
8	9	7	6	4	2	1	3	5
3	2	4	5	1	8	7	9	6

WORD WHEEL FROM PAGE 119 The nine-letter word is SCRAPHEAP

We'll Meet Again...

Twice in her life Lily had been uprooted and started afresh. But the memories lingered on...

By Jean Robinson

Lily opened the envelope with trembling hands. It was the first time she'd heard from him in over a year. Even now she could feel a warmth spread through her as she stared at the carefully crafted letter in that familiar neat writing. Dear Phil. She still missed him

"What is it, love?" her mum asked, watching in concern.

"It's from Phil. Aunt Lou's in hospital. She's been asking for me."

"Then you must go. You owe her that, Lily. She was like a mother to you when you were evacuated with her during the war."

"I know, Mum, but I've got work. It's a long way and I can't just take a day off."

"Well, you can go on Saturday, then."

All day Lily typed away in the office, her mind constantly on Aunt Lou. The situation must be serious for Phil to write to her after all this time.

In the end, she asked her boss if she could leave early. She might be able to get there for the evening visiting time. Saturday was two days off, and she needed to see Aunt Lou now.

He smiled at her indulgently.

"Go, lass. You're not much good here today. That's the third time I've asked you to type that letter."

She apologised but his smile was warm.

"You're a good worker, Lily. It must be important for you to ask a favour."

She quickly explained the situation as he hurried her out of the building.

On the train to Southport, her mind went back to the first time she'd made this journey. It was 1939 and war was about to break out.

The memory was forever etched in her mind. A nine-year-old girl standing on the station clutching a small brown suitcase, a label with a number on it

"Don't cry, Lily. We're going to the seaside. It'll be just like a holiday"

strung round her neck and a gas mask hanging from her shoulder. There were hundreds of children milling round, and some of the teachers who'd brought them from school.

"Don't cry, Lily," her older brother Freddie had said, trying to comfort her. "We're going to the seaside. It'll be just like a holiday."

But Lily knew it wouldn't be. They ➤

were going to live with strangers and it wouldn't be like that at all.

"Then why's our mum not coming?" Lily sobbed, trying hard to hold back the tears. Freddie shrugged as if he didn't know either.

Mum had told her to be brave. That it wouldn't be for long.

She stared round at the other children. Some were laughing and chattering as if it was a Sunday school outing. Others were standing alone and looking as frightened as she felt. It was the first time she'd ever been away from her mum – except to go to school, of course.

When the train drew into the station the adults began to pack children into the carriages with much pushing and shouting. Eventually Lily found herself squashed up against the window beside a large girl who kept looking at her and scowling as if it was Lily who was taking up all the room.

Lily would rather have stayed with her mum and taken her chance.

Freddie had sat opposite her peering out of the carriage window, eyes wide as they drew out of the station. Neither of them had ever been on a train before.

He became more excited as the train rumbled along on what seemed to Lily to be an endless journey.

"Look, Lil, look at those big sand hills. I never seen anything like that before,"

She hadn't wanted to look. She wanted to go home to her mum and their little terraced house in the big city.

Once off the train they were taken by bus to a big hall already packed with noisy children. The people in charge were trying to line them up and keep order. Lily watched fearfully as women moved down the lines looking them over. A child would be pulled out, then either pushed back in place or marched off.

"You look clean and decent. I'll take you," the lady said, taking Lily's arm

Lily stared out at the platform. Some of the mothers had come to see their children off and were scanning the carriages for their offspring, then waving frantically. Lily's mum had stayed at home, saying that the goodbyes would be too painful. Lily wished she was there waving with the rest.

Sitting on the train now, thirteen years later, Lily could still feel that heart-wrenching pain she'd experienced then at leaving her home and her mum for a reason she didn't quite understand – only that it was something about a war and maybe bombs falling on Liverpool and they'd all be in danger, so they were being taken far away to Southport where they would be safe.

A miserable-looking woman approached Lily, then – after looking her up and down – she moved on.

Even now Lily could feel the humiliation of that rejection. How she had looked down at her feet and seen that her shoes were scuffed and her socks were not as white as those of the girl standing next to her, and the realisation that she was not good enough to be chosen.

Then a tall, severe-looking lady had pushed her way through. "You look clean and decent. I'll take you," she'd said, taking Lily's arm.

But Lily wasn't going anywhere without Freddie. The lady saw how she gripped his hand.

"Well, now, who's the young man you're hanging on to?"

"He's my brother," Lily managed through trembling lips.

"Then we'd better take him, too," the lady said.

Relief was overwhelming as both children were escorted out of the hall.

"Now, you don't need to be afraid. I'm going to look after you and keep you safe until this nasty war's over. You can call me Aunt Lou," she told them as, one each side of her, she hurried them to the bus stop.

Lily's eyes opened wide when she saw the big Victorian house they were taken to. There was a garden in front of it and a long path to the front door. She'd never seen anything like it before. The front door at home opened onto a busy road.

Inside they were taken down a long hallway to a room at the back which Aunt Lou called the kitchen. But it was nothing like the kitchen at home. There was a fire in a big black grate, and a big oak table and chairs, and a couch along one wall.

"Now, this is Phillip. He's my big boy," Aunt Lou announced as a tall, broad-shouldered boy with a pleasant face came into the room.

He was followed by a skinny girl who looked at them with distaste. She was introduced as Gladys. Lily thought how grand that sounded. She'd never heard the name before.

"Now, you two, I want you to make Freddie and Lily feel at home here. They will be part of our family until the danger of war is over. I'll leave you children to get to know each other while I get dinner

ready," Aunt Lou told them, then disappeared into a room even further back in the house.

"Why do you have to come and live in our house?" Gladys shot at Lily. "Haven't you got a home of your own?"

"They're evacuees," Phil reminded her.

"Mum explained about it. But you never listen."

"The Germans are going to bomb Liverpool because it's a big and important city. We've come here to be safe," Freddie added.

"Well, I don't see why we have to have you. What have you got in your case there?" Gladys asked.

"Clothes and things," Lily said timidly.

"Where are you going to sleep?"

"Don't know."

Lily was on the verge of tears again but determined not to break down in front of these other children. How she longed for her own little bed in the corner of her mum's bedroom.

Over dinner, which they ate with relish, Aunt Lou explained they would have to share bedrooms – Lily with Gladys and Freddie with Phil.

"Couldn't I share with Freddie?" Lily asked nervously.

"Oh, dear, no. That wouldn't be proper," Aunt Lou said.

"Well, I don't want her in my room," Gladys piped up.

"Gladys!" Aunt Lou said, giving her a sharp look. Gladys left the table in a sulk.

Lily sniffed back a sob. How would she ever fit into this family? If only she could go home to her mum she wouldn't mind how many bombs fell round them. ➤

"hy isn't your dad away at war?" Lily asked Gladys one day as they were helping Phil collect eggs from the hen house in the back yard.

"He's in a reserved occupation," Gladys told her proudly.

This didn't enlighten Lily at all as to what Uncle George did. He was a shadowy figure who was seldom around and kept himself to himself, often behind a newspaper.

"What about yours?" Gladys asked.

"I don't have a dad," Lily said.

"Everyone has a dad," Gladys said, scornfully.

Tears sprang to Lily's eyes and she brushed them away angrily.

Phil told Gladys not to be so nasty. If Lily said she didn't have a dad, then she didn't. He often came to her rescue in these situations.

and she told him she didn't want to know. Yet, even though she listened in fear and trembling, she still hung on his every word. She visualised their home in ruins and wondered what would happen to her mum then.

Lily sat anxiously while Uncle George listened to the radio in the evening. He'd notice her worried face and smile reassuringly.

"No need to worry, little one. No bombs last night."

Aunt Lou was the kindest person anyone could have wished for. They were well fed and cared for. Freddie and Phil got on well. If only Gladys hadn't been so mean, Lily thought she could have been happy. As it was, it took her a long time to settle. She missed her mum and the friends she used to play with

She sobbed under the blanket to try to stifle the sound in case she woke Gladys

When the bombing began in Liverpool Lily became increasingly worried about her mum. What if a bomb fell on her house? She questioned Aunt Lou about it.

"Your mum will be safe," Aunt Lou reassured her. "They get a warning when the Germans are coming over with their planes and they all go into air raid shelters, and they don't come out until they get the all clear."

Letters from her mum had told her about her nights in these shelters. It all sounded quite jolly, with people singing to keep up their spirits. But Lily didn't think she'd like to have to spend the night in one. Freddie had told her that sometimes they came out of them in the morning and their house would be a pile of rubble after being hit by a bomb. It made her shudder

down at the Rec.

Aunt Lou took them on long walks on the beach at weekends and sometimes, when the weather was warm, she'd pack a picnic with whatever she could rustle up from their rations. Best of all was when Aunt Lou took them to visit her sister in Ainsdale and they could romp around in the sand dunes.

It was only in the night when she woke after a bad dream that she longed for the comforting presence of her mum and the way she would rock her gently back to sleep. On these occasions she'd sob under the blanket to try to stifle the sound in case she woke Gladys.

During the week Phil and Gladys went off to school each morning. Lily wondered why she and Freddie didn't go with them.

"There aren't enough places for you

lot," Gladys told her.

Aunt Lou explained that they would find a place in a school for them as soon as they could, but there were a lot of evacuee children all needing places and the schools couldn't cope.

Then one morning Aunt Lou told her they'd found places for both of them. Although Lily was pleased, she was a little disappointed when she discovered it was not the same school that Phil went to. He had become her hero, always looking out for her, especially when Gladys was in a mean mood.

Her first day at school was intimidating but she soon made friends and began to look forward to going.

But Freddie was becoming restless and told her one day that he was going home.

"Am I going, too?" she asked Aunt Lou excitedly.

"No, dear, there are still risks of bombs falling. I don't think Freddie should go but he's determined. He hasn't settled like you. A lot of evacuees are returning home. But your mum wants you to stay a little longer. You're happy here, aren't you, dear?"

Lily bit her lip and tried not to cry. She hadn't been home once since arriving off that train. And her mum had only come to visit a couple of times.

Aunt Lou gave her a hug and told her it wouldn't be long. This nasty war would soon be over and then she could go home.

"And look how well you're doing at school. Your mum's keen for you to get a good education and the school you used to go to has closed down due to the war."

Over the next few days Lily tried to think about all this. It would only be for a short time. She did enjoy school. And she had Aunt Lou. And Phil. They had grown close, and he seemed more of a brother to her now than Freddie, who had become morose and edgy when she spoke to him.

As the war drew to a close Lily knew it was finally time to go home. Aunt Lou had made it clear that she would be welcome to stay on if she wanted to.

"That is if your mum is agreeable, of course," she'd added.

This left Lily undecided. She'd lived with Aunt Lou for so long now she could hardly remember living anywhere else. But her home was still in Liverpool with her mum and Freddie, and she didn't want to hurt them. Her mum could do with the wages she would be able to bring home once she left school and got a job.

Part of her felt she should return to where she belonged. She loved her mum and still missed her, but it would be hard to leave Aunt Lou and the place she had come to look on as home. And she wouldn't have Phil to talk to in the evenings. Just her grumpy brother.

She pondered this endlessly for weeks. Her mind was finally made up when Phil told her he had a girlfriend and was taking her to the pictures.

"He's courting," Aunt Lou explained when she saw Lily's face. "He's not a boy any more. He"s a man."

Lily knew this. Phil had already left school and was working. But the ➤

girlfriend bit came as a shock. She decided there and then that it was time for her to move on as well, and she planned to go back home as soon as she could leave school in a couple of months' time.

Even now, years later, she could recall that unbearable anguish of teenage love. His betrayal was a bitter hurt she had kept hidden inside her as she tried to deal with the aching loneliness of knowing her friend and ally now had someone more important in his life.

When Lily returned home, her mum was delighted. But it took her a long time to settle once more. An outside toilet. Noisy traffic passing the front door. Her brother had become estranged and was more interested in girls than in his kid sister. Her mum seemed to have grown old and careworn, dragged down by the

news, and something stopped Lily from asking. It was all in the past, and that was where she wanted it to stay.

Then one Christmas the card had a short letter enclosed. Phil had become engaged to a lovely girl and Aunt Lou seemed very excited about it. Lily was shocked at how much this affected her, even though she had been going out with Jake for several months now and thought they might end up together.

As the train drew slowly into Chapel Street station in Southport, Lily's heart grew tight. She hadn't been able to contact Phil at such short notice to tell him she was on her way.

Part of her hoped he would be there at the hospital when she arrived. Yet she was nervous at the thought of seeing him again after so long.

All the way there in the taxi, Lily's

Across the bed Phil's eyes met Lily's and something passed between them

trauma of war. But it was home, and this was her real family.

Outings with Phil, when she'd meet him off the train in Liverpool and he'd take her to a Lyon's Corner House for tea, were the highlight of her life. There was never any mention of the girlfriend and Lily didn't ask.

Slowly she adjusted, took a secretarial course and found herself a job with a firm of solicitors. Then she met Jake. Finally life seemed good again.

When National Service took Phil away to France, their only communication had been by letter. Eventually these ceased.

She still thought about Phil, wondered what he was doing, and whether he ever thought about her. Aunt Lou always sent her a card for her birthday and one at Christmas. But there was seldom any

anxiety increased. What would she find when she arrived? Phil had said little in the letter, just that Aunt Lou was in hospital and asking for her. It sounded serious, and she was afraid.

There was an element of guilt too. She should have made more effort to keep in touch once the war had ended and she'd gone home – maybe paid a visit more often. But life had got in the way. Now she feared it might be too late.

At first Lily didn't recognize the smart young man who rose to greet her when the nurse showed her into the ward. She was shocked to see how frail Aunt Lou looked lying there in the hospital bed, but relieved to see she could still manage a smile when she saw her.

She cautiously gave her a tearful hug

and then sat beside her, still holding her hand.

"Mum's going to be all right," Phil reassured Lily. "She had a heart attack but they say she's recovering well."

Phil gave his mum an affectionate smile.

"He's a good son," Aunt Lou whispered to Lily.

Sitting either side of the hospital bed, Phil's eyes met Lily's and something passed between them that had her heart racing. Quickly she looked away, feeling self-conscious and confused.

Aunt Lou began to look more animated as Lily chatted to her about home and her job and what Freddie was doing.

"You've cheered me up no end," Aunt Lou told Lily as she kissed her goodbye with the promise of another visit soon.

In the canteen later over a cup of tea Lily began to feel more relaxed with Phil as they chatted about old times, how Gladys had toned down her antagonistic behaviour and was now working in a posh shoe shop on Lord Street.

He told Lily how much he had missed her once she had gone home.

She told him about Jake.

"I never married," he told her.

Lily raised an eyebrow.

"Your mum said you were engaged."

He shook his head sadly.

"I was. But eventually Jen ended it. She knew there was something amiss. And it would have been wrong for me to deny it. She deserved better than to marry a man whose heart lay elsewhere. She told me I was still yearning after you. I hadn't realized how much I talked about you."

Lily didn't know how to respond to this and, after a short silence, Phil looked up from the teacup he'd been staring at.

"There's never been anyone who could take your place," he said, giving her a wistful smile.

"Why did you never tell me?" she asked in a shaky voice.

"I suppose it didn't feel quite right, us being brought up like brother and sister." He paused and held her eyes for a moment. "I don't feel that way now."

Phil saw her to the station to catch the last train home.

"I'll keep in touch," he told her. "To let you know how Aunt Lou is progressing."

They were standing on the platform facing each other as they waited for the train to arrive, the distance between them bristling with uncertainty.

Lily longed so much to move closer and fall into his arms. But that would have to wait. They had a lot of catching up to do first.

Tomorrow she would tell Jake. He would be devastated, but she knew she could not continue with their relationship. Not now she had finally accepted that her first love would be her one and only love – and knew that it was returned. **MW**

· ·

ACT OF KINDNESS

During an illness, my teenage granddaughter, knowing how I love walking in the countryside, took me on virtual walks with her every day via our mobiles, chatting and pointing out views. It was the highlight of my day.

Special Journey

This meeting at the end of the pier was different...

By Lynda Franklin

I t was one of those unexpected beautiful December mornings, the air crisp with the chill of winter and the sky as bright and blue as summer. Pippa paused to watch the sea gulls dip and dive in the cold sunshine before boarding the train, the sound of their greedy screeching filling her ears.

She found a seat quickly and stared out of the window, determined to find something to look at, something to keep her mind busy during the short journey. The seat was hard and upright and soon being kicked rhythmically by a small child sitting behind. It didn't matter. Not today. She didn't care about anything today.

Glancing into her bag for the hundredth time she took out her purse. Opening it, she gazed at the prized possession for a few seconds, before closing it again and putting it back into the sanctity of her handbag. She must have checked it a hundred times since leaving home, and would probably check it a hundred more before getting off the train.

She sat back in the hard chair, mentally counting the kicks to her back. How many would there be before she reached her destination? The mother was blissfully unaware. How many kicks, she wondered, before she was? Pippa began to count ➤

all over again. It was something to do.

After a while, she took a quick glance around to see who was making all the noise in the carriage. The family was large – all ages – the little ones kneeling on the seats pointing and calling out. The adults were mostly ignoring them, too busy with their own loud dialogues to intervene. Pippa forced herself to look away and out of the window again, drifting to a safe place in her mind. They were all in this train, all going to the same place, all for different reasons. It was such an ordinary thing to do on this blowy winter's day, but this day was far from ordinary. She fought the urge to check her purse again.

There were only a few minutes to go now. The kicking had stopped. Finally the mother had noticed and whispered to the child. Pippa stopped counting.

Last time she came she was holding a

train stopped, the loud family jumped off. Pippa could see them walking away together, little ones holding hands, bigger ones running ahead, adults still talking.

Pippa stood up, breathing deeply to ease the nervous feeling that refused to go.

Stepping off the little pier train and on to the pier, she saw her husband Matthew immediately. He'd slipped out of work in his lunch hour to meet her because he understood how important it was for them to be here. In this place. Together.

"Don't forget, now," she'd reminded him earlier.

"Of course I won't forget." He took a last sip of tea. "How could I forget?"

This was where she first saw him ten years ago. Southend Pier, leaning against the railings, hair blowing in the wind, slightly tanned with a smile that still made her heart flip. It had been Carnival week

Matthew. The thought of him made her smile and feel warm inside

balloon. It had waved frantically in the breeze as if alive and desperate to go its own way and she had to grip it tightly in her hand. Once she brought a blue one.

She particularly remembered that blue balloon because it slowly deflated during the journey, and when she got off the train it hovered in the air only a few seconds before dropping to the ground. She hadn't brought a balloon this time.

Maybe she should have brought something else, but she couldn't think of anything to bring. In the end she decided it didn't matter. Matthew never liked the balloon thing anyway.

Matthew. The thought of him made her smile and feel warm inside.

The steady drum of the train wheels was slowing. The mother sitting behind grabbed the toddler with restless legs, half carrying, half dragging him off. As the

and the pier was buzzing. He was larking around with a group of his friends, young and carefree. She knew he liked her because he was showing off, and she liked that he was trying to impress her.

He bought her a coffee and they ended up going to the amusement park. She remembered the rides, how exciting it had been as it grew dark, the coloured lights and music drowning out their conversation. He'd held her hand and made her laugh until it hurt.

Eventually they had to say goodbye, but he got on the bus with her. To make sure she got home OK, he said.

He still worried about her.

Matthew was smiling at her now. She waved and fiddled with her bag. It gave her some much-needed time. Emotion was bubbling so near the surface

now she was having difficulty controlling it.

She knew what she wanted to say – hadn't she rehearsed it a thousand times?

The sun was still shining even though there was no warmth in it. They were lucky. Sometimes when they came, it was raining. Once it had snowed, and they had to walk the mile and more to the end of the pier because the train wasn't running. But neither of them had cared. It had to be here. They always came here. Usually with a balloon. But not this time.

He was walking towards her now and she noticed he was wearing black jeans and his usual blue anorak. A red scarf was blowing wildly around his neck.

She noticed his hair needed cutting, and that although he was smiling, there was an uncertain look on his face. She noticed because she wanted to notice. She wanted to remember every single thing about today.

"Hi, babe." He kissed her cheek and took her hand. Pippa suddenly felt vulnerable without her balloon. Perhaps she should have brought one anyway.

Neither said anything for a while. It was as if they were both frightened to break the spell. So far, this was normal. So far, this was what they did each time. They would walk on to the end of the pier, their special place, and sit on their special seat overlooking the sea. Matthew would pour coffee from his flask for them both. They would watch the blue-grey waters swirling beneath them through the gaps in the planked walkway, and set their balloon free.

Usually it would soar towards the heavens, and that would help somehow. When the blue one died before their eyes, the heartbreak felt like a searing pain.

"More coffee?" Matthew asked her.

Pippa shook her head, aware her hand holding the cup was shaking slightly.

"Are you cold?"

"No. I'm fine."

"I've brought sandwiches. In case you fancy something."

Pippa smiled. "I'm not hungry."

"We could get something hot from the café if you like."

"But we don't usually, do we?"

It had to be the same.

Matthew took the cup from her. "You're right. We don't. I just thought –"

"No," Pippa said softly, pulling her coat around tightly and resting her head against his shoulder. She watched the gulls struggling in the stiff breeze and noticed white choppy foam appearing on the waves. The air felt bitterly cold against her face and she was glad of it. She didn't ever remember sitting at the end of the pier without a bracing fresh wind blowing. It was part of it. Nothing must be ➔

different. Apart from one thing.

"No balloon today," Matthew eventually said.

"No," she whispered. There was so much she intended to say. Where had her prepared speech gone? In the train it had been in her head, like a disc on repeat, word perfect. Why was her mind now so blank? Where were the special words she had chosen so carefully?

"Sorry, I couldn't get away from work. I wanted to be there."

"It doesn't matter." She smiled at him. "It's going to be all right. They promised this time."

He smiled back. "Show me," he said.

The blue sky was streaked with grey and white now as the wind got fiercer, and spray from the choppy waves rose into the air like a gossamer wall. Seagulls shrieked as they looked for thrown away food, and the atmosphere echoed with sound – crashing water, loud voices, laughter and squeals as the waves found their target. Pippa opened her bag, oblivious to the outside world.

She took out her purse and passed the treasured possession to Matthew. He held it tightly in both hands, scared the wind would blow it away, staring into it. He looked for a long while, taking in every detail, and when he gave the small scan picture back, his eyes were bright.

Pippa squeezed his hand.

"Our baby," she said. "Our little Christmas miracle. At last."

Matthew nodded, looking out across the darkening ocean. No more disappointments. No more heart-rending farewells. No more balloons.

"More coffee?" he said, his voice thick with emotion.

Pippa shook her head. "Caffeine isn't good for me."

Mathew smiled. "I guess not."

"Should we have a toast maybe?"

"We don't need speeches, Pippa." Matthew was right. No words could make this moment more special than it was. Didn't they both know already how desperately loved and wanted this child would be?

They huddled close to keep warm, gazing out at the rough sea and changing landscape. They sat for a long time, talking and planning, until the pale sun finally began to sink in glorious milky red.

"The last train goes soon," Matthew said.

Pippa nodded. The pier was empty now. Only the gulls wailed and screamed as they walked to the station and boarded the train. They were the only ones sitting on the hard upright chairs now, staring out into the vanishing daylight as waves lapped and splashed either side of the track, as the pier began to pull down the shutters and finish for the day.

Pippa stroked her stomach gently, listening to the steady beat of the wheels taking them all the way back to the shore and home. (MW)

ACT OF KINDNESS

The past months have certainly been difficult, and when my 10 year old granddaughter gave me a homemade necklace with a four leaf clover in the middle 'to keep me safe', it meant more than anything.